Flying Training
Volume 1

Dorothy Pooley

POOLEYS

Nothing in this manual supersedes any legislation, rules, regulations or procedures contained in any operational document issued by Her Majesty's Stationery Office, the Civil Aviation Authority, the Joint Aviation Authorities, ICAO, the manufacturers of aircraft, engines and systems, or by the operators of aircraft throughout the world.

Flying Training, Volume 1

Pooley Aviation Ltd
Mill Road
Cranfield, Beds
MK43 0JG
England

Tel: 01234 750677
Fax: 01234 750706
sales@pooleys.com
www.pooleys.com

Editorial Team

AUTHOR
Dorothy Pooley LLB(Hons) FRAeS
Dorothy holds an ATPL and is both an instructor and examiner, running Flight Instructor courses at Shoreham and she is Training Captain for an AOC operator also at Shoreham. She is also a CAA Flight Instructor Examiner. In addition, having qualified as a solicitor in 1982, Dorothy acts as a consultant to ASB Law, where she specialises in aviation and insurance liability issues. She has lectured widely on Air Law and insurance issues. This highly unusual combination of qualifications has led to her nomination as an expert in aviation law and her appointment as Honorary Solicitor to the Guild of Air Pilots and Air Navigators (GAPAN). A Fellow of the Royal Aeronautical Society, she chairs the GAPAN Instructor Committee, and is on the Education & Training Committee, as well as serving as an Assistant on their Court. In 2003 Dorothy was awarded the Jean Lennox Bird Trophy for her contribution to aviation and support of Women in Aviation and the BWPA (British Women Pilots Association). A regular contributor to seminars and conferences, Dorothy is the author and editor of a number of flying training books and has published articles in legal and insurance journals.

EDITORS
Peter Godwin FRIN
Head of Training at Bonus Aviation, Cranfield (formerly Leavesden Flight Centre), Peter has amassed over 14,000 instructional flying hours as a fixed-wing and helicopter instructor. As a member of the CAA Panel of Examiners, he is a CAA Flight Examiner for the Private Pilot's Licence (FEPPL(A)), Flight Instructor Examiner (FIE(A)), as well as an Instrument Rating and Class Rating Examiner. A Fellow of the Royal Institute of Navigation (FRIN), Peter is currently training flying instructors and applicants for the Commercial Pilot's Licence and Instrument Rating. He has been Vice Chairman and subsequently Chairman of the Flight Training Committee on behalf of the General Aviation Manufacturers' and Traders' Association (GAMTA) since 1992 and is a regular lecturer at AOPA Flight Instructor Seminars. In 1999 Peter was awarded the Pike Trophy by the Guild of Air Pilots and Air Navigators for his contribution to the maintenance of high standards of flying instruction and flight safety. Previously he was Chief Pilot for an air charter company and Chief Instructor for the Cabair group of companies based at Denham and Elstree.

Daljeet Gill BA(Hons)
Daljeet is Head of Design & Development for Pooleys Flight Equipment and editor of the Pooleys Private Pilots Guides, Pre-flight Briefing, R/T Communications, Pooleys ATPL Manuals and Air Presentation, Ground School Training Transparencies plus many others. Daljeet has been involved with editing, typesetting and design for all these publications. Graduated in 1999 with a BA (hons) in Graphic Design, she deals with marketing, advertising & design of our new products. She maintains our website and produces our Pooleys Catalogue annually. Her input on this publication is obvious.

Helena Hughes BA(Hons)
The author of the Radiotelephony manual in this series, Helena is an Air Traffic Controller and Flying Instructor with a CPL/IR.

Acknowledgements

This publication could not have been made possible without the valuable contribution of many friends and colleagues. Particularly, we would like to thank David Duckworth, Nicolas Chan and the late Ron Campbell whose influence on flying training is seminal. Many others have offered their thoughts and advice, too many to mention, but we must also thank the CAA who offered their support throughout.

Preface

This Volume 1, Flying Training is also designed to be used in conjunction with Air Presentations Pre-flight Briefings. As a student you will find that this book gives you the background reading material (theory) to accompany your briefing. For the instructor, this book will enhance the briefing material and the Guide for Instructors. Whether you rely on the spiral-bound paper form of Pre-Flight Briefings, or you use the overhead projector slides, or Powerpoint, the reading of the appropriate chapter before your lesson will facilitate the briefing process and assist your learning, accelerating your progress in the air. Completing the quizzes will also assist you in your understanding, enabling you to pass your Ground School Examinations with ease. The whole integrated package is designed to be interactive, colourful and easy to use.

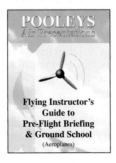

Contents

Flying Training Manual

Introduction

"For I dipt into the future, far as human eye could see,
Saw the Vision of the world, and all the wonder that would be;
Saw the heavens fill with commerce, argosies of magic sails,
Pilots of the purple twilight, dropping down with costly bales..."

Alfred, Lord Tennyson(1809-1892)
From "Locksley Hall"

Ever since the earliest times, man has sought to "slip the surly bonds of earth" and emulate his feathered friends in flight. Ancient legend tells of Icarus, whose fragile craft of wax and feathers flew too close to the sun, which melted the wax thus precipitating his fall to tragedy. In the 15th century the inspired imagination of Leonardo da Vinci created intricate designs for flying machines, way ahead of his time.

For centuries the ability to lift man's weight from the earth eluded the inventors, but in 1783 the Montgolfier brothers achieved this feat when Pilatre de Rozier and the Marquis d'Arlandes were lifted across Paris in a hot air balloon. Since then the development of flight has been rapid and accelerating, although it is perhaps hard to comprehend that it is barely a century since the Wright Brothers' historic achievement at Kitti Hawk, North Carolina, USA.

Of course, the Wright brothers had to teach themselves to fly which was a slow and often painful process of learning. There were few books of theory and little experience on which to base the learning experience. As aircraft have evolved and developed, it has become clear that there are two vitally important factors which will assist the would-be pilot and accelerate the learning process - 1) a skilled and patient instructor and 2) a good manual of instruction. Whilst we cannot guarantee your choice of instructor, we can hope that this Manual will assist you in your endeavours to learn to be a pilot.

You will see that the layout of this book is designed to interact and cross-refer to the other books in the series. Additionally you will notice extensive cross-referral to the series of Air Presentations overhead projector slides. Together with the student workbooks you have an integrated learning package to provide you with comprehensive guidance throughout your course.

Learning To Fly

The whole process of learning to fly can be achieved in a number of ways. You may elect to attend an intensive course of training over a period of a few weeks or you may learn more slowly taking your lessons once or twice a week over a number of months. Whichever method you choose, you will need to integrate your ground school and theory study with the practical flying training.

Some schools offer a programme of ground school lectures; whilst the majority of people will study on their own, it is always worth attending any lectures offered as they will provide an opportunity to clear up any doubts or confusion as well as giving you a different perspective n the subject-matter. To assist you with your training and learning, each chapter in this manual contains aims and learning objectives. We have included short quizzes and tests for you to check your understanding on how much reading ahead to undertake to prepare for each lesson. You will find your learning accelerates if you do prepare in advance.

It is advisable to obtain a copy of the PPL Syllabus and Student's Record of Training which will give you detailed guidance for your course and includes cross-references to ground school subjects.

Any of these three Syllabuses & Student Record of Training booklets is strongly recommended during your training to safeguard your progress with your school.

Some Technical Stuff before we Start!

What Makes an Aircraft Fly?

This is the sort of question that children like to ask their parents, in the league of "**where does the wind come from**" or "**why is there a rainbow**"? If you studied science at school you will probably have some idea of what makes an aircraft fly, but if your education was lacking in that respect you may genuinely have no idea. Whilst it is not especially important at the stage of a trial lesson to understand the principles of flight, it does become important as you progress towards obtaining your licence. It may interest you to have some insight at this early stage of your training in which case it is worth reading this section before continuing to the air exercises.

The force needed to keep an aircraft in the air is called lift. This is produced by forcing the air to flow over the wings and tailplane. The construction of the wings and tailplane are such that if you looked at the cross section through them you would see a shape as below, which is called an aerofoil section.

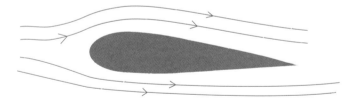

AEROFOIL

This is important, as the shape causes the air flowing over the top surface of the wing to travel further and therefore faster than that passing underneath it. The faster flowing air generates an area of slightly lower pressure on the top surface and effectively the wing is "sucked" up into the lower pressure air above it. This is what holds the wing up!

Lift is produced independently of power from the engine - this is why a glider can fly! What the engine produces is called thrust. The thrust is needed to get the aircraft moving along the runway in the first place and is also required to overcome drag. Some of the drag is the by-product of lift, the force which resists the movement of the aircraft through the air. *(As a child you may have experienced this by holding your hand out of the car window as it accelerated down the road.)* The other force involved is weight. The weight of the aircraft determines how much lift is required to get it into the air. The arrangement of these forces is shown on the diagram below. As long as the lift produced by the wings is enough to overcome the weight and the thrust produced by the engine is enough to overcome the drag, then the aircraft will fly. Even if the engine stops, if you allow the aircraft to descend in a glide, the airspeed resulting will be high enough to generate sufficient lift to keep the aircraft gliding down, rather like a car coasting down a hill.

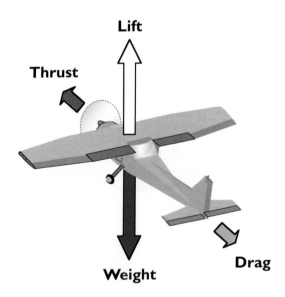

Four Forces

1. Aircraft Controls

1.1 Elevator

On aircraft such as the Cessna, the elevator is a hinged surface on the rear of the fixed tailplane. On some Piper aircraft the whole tailplane surface moves and this is called a stabilator. Applying forward pressure to the control column causes the elevator to move down and increase the lift over the tailplane. This results in the nose of the aircraft pitching down. The converse results from applying backpressure.

Pitch

1.2 Ailerons

Rotating the control column to the left causes the left aileron to move up and the right aileron to move down. This results in an increase of lift on the right wing causing it to rise and the reduction of lift on the left wing causes it to lower. The aircraft will therefore roll to the left. The reverse will occur if the control column is rotated to the right.

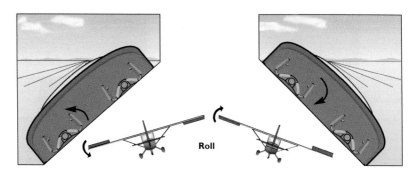

Roll

1.3   Rudder

On the ground the rudder pedals are used for steering the aircraft and to operate the brakes. To taxy the aircraft, your heels should be on the floor to avoid inadvertently applying the brakes - the same applies for take-off and landing. To operate the brakes you slide your feet up the pedals to pivot the top portion forwards. To turn the aircraft on the ground, simply pressing the right pedal will turn the aircraft right and vice versa. Applying the brake during the turn will tighten up the turn.

In flight the rudder, hinged on the rear of the vertical tailfin is also operated by the rudder pedals. Pressing the right rudder now moves the rudder to the right, skidding the nose of the aircraft to the right (yaw) and pressing the left pedal will skid the nose to the left. This is neither a comfortable nor efficient way of making a turn and normally the rudder will be used in coordination with the ailerons to produce a balanced and comfortable turn.

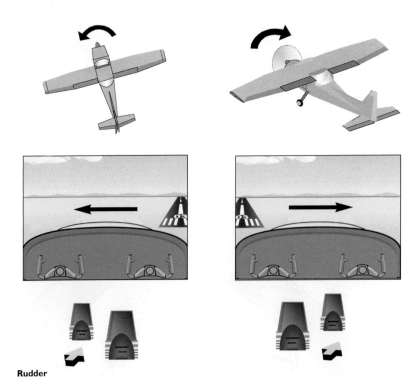

Rudder

2. Engine Controls

2.1 Throttle

This is a lever or push/pull control usually positioned in the control panel between the pilots or on a separate "quadrant". It works like the accelerator in your car - pressing it into the panel will increase the power and pulling it out will reduce the power. Pulling the throttle fully out does not stop the engine, simply allows it to tick over or "idle" just like a car engine.

Throttle

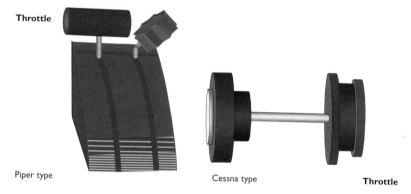

Piper type   Cessna type   **Throttle**

2.2 Carburettor Heat

This is another lever or push/pull control which is used to direct hot air into the carburettor intake to prevent ice from forming and blocking the intake. The design of a carburettor means that this problem may occur in conditions of high relative humidity or when there is a low power setting, so its use is a safety factor and you will see your instructor using the "carb heat" regularly during the flight.

Carburettor Heat

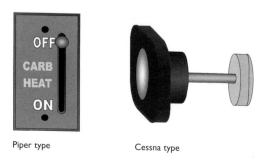

Piper type   Cessna type

2.3 Mixture

The mixture control is usually coloured red for danger! If pulled fully out, the engine will stop as the fuel flow will be cut off. The lever can be used in flight to set the correct mixture of fuel and air for optimum performance from the engine. At altitude the air becomes thinner *(you may have experienced this if you have been up a mountain)* and unless this procedure is carried out the engine would not run efficiently.

Piper Mixture Control

Cessna Mixture Control

3. Other Controls

3.1 Trimwheel

This is used to remove any forward or backward pressure on the control column which would otherwise make the flying tiring for the pilot. It is usually possible to trim the aircraft "hands off" so that there is little or no input required to hold the aircraft in the attitude set by the pilot.

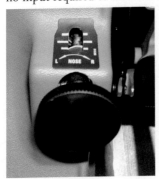

Trimwheels (Rudder)

Piper Trimweel Elevator

3.2   Flap Lever

This may be an electrical switch *(as in a Cessna 152)* or a lever that looks like the handbrake in a car *(in a Piper)*. Operating the flap selector allows a section of the wing which is hinged to extend downward and/or rearwards into the airflow, increasing lift *(and thereby drag)*. This helps in the landing of the aircraft.

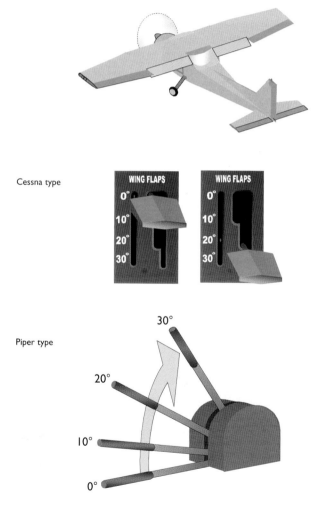

Cessna type

Piper type

Type of Flap Levers

3.3 Brakes

As previously stated these are generally operated by pressing the tops of the rudder pedals although in some older aircraft, such as the Piper Cub, heelbrakes may be fitted. The principle is the same. There is also often a parking brake fitted. This is not often a very sophisticated system in light aircraft and should not be relied on, so you will probably see your instructor "covering" the brakes with his or her feet when (s)he carries out the power checks, to ensure that the aircraft does not slip forwards.

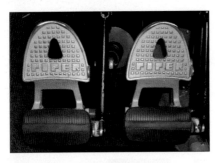 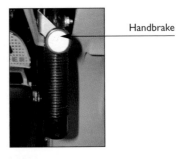

Handbrake

4. Radios & Intercom

The radio is needed for communications with Air Traffic Control. This is important to obtain clearance for take-off and landing. You will hear lots of abbreviations and codes being spoken over the radio. There is a special "language" for the radio communications to ensure that valuable airtime is not wasted. For further infomation see Volume 5 in this series of manuals.

5. Instruments

PA38 Piper Tomahawk

5.1 Attitude Indicator *(Artificial Horizon)*

This instrument can be used to judge the amount of pitch or bank angle being applied, but it is generally only relied on if the aircraft is flying in cloud, by sole reference to instruments. Otherwise pitch and bank are judged by looking outside at the horizon.

5.2 Magnetic Compass & Direction Indicator

Since a compass is very sensitive and moves about a lot when the aircraft is flying, a direction indicator ("**DI**") is usually fitted to complement the magnetic compass and show heading information. The DI has to be aligned with the magnetic compass regularly to prevent errors developing. Headings are usually worked out relative to magnetic north.

5.3 Altimeter

This instrument operates on the principle of a barometer. It shows the pilot how high the aircraft is, by measuring the air pressure. As the pressure changes on a daily basis, it is necessary to set the correct datum for the sea level pressure in a sub-scale on the instrument. This will ensure that the correct reading is displayed on the dial.

5.4 Airspeed Indicator

A pilot needs to know that the correct speed for take-off has been achieved, as a minimum speed will be required to develop enough lift over the wings. The dial usually has a colour coded system for displaying the various limits of speeds appropriate to the aircraft.

5.5 Vertical Speed Indicator

This instrument shows rate of climb or descent in 100's of feet per minute.

5.6 Turn Co-ordinator & Balance Ball

This is a combined instrument. It shows rate of turn of the aircraft and has a glass tube containing a ball in some fluid, which works a bit like a spirit level. The movement of the ball during turning manoeuvres shows skid, slip or yaw as the ball is displaced from its central position to the edge of the glass tube by centrifugal force.

5.7 Tachometer (rpm)

This is similar to the rev counter in your car. The green band shows the normal operating range for the aircraft when it is in the cruise.

5.8 Temperature & Pressure Gauges

These little gauges are very important for the monitoring of the health of the engine. Again, green bands will indicate the normal operating range and any deviation outside these green bands should alert the pilot to question what is happening.

Left Intentionally Blank

Chapter 1

Familiarisation with the Aeroplane

1.1 LESSON AIM

To learn the general characteristics of the aeroplane.

LESSON OBJECTIVE

By the end of the lesson you will be able to state and identify accurately the main characteristics of your training aeroplane.

AIRMANSHIP

Pilot Knowledge. Definition of Airmanship.

Introduction

External & Internal Characteristics

Cessna 152

Piper Cherokee PA28

The photograph overleaf shows two different types of training aeroplane. Although there are many types of aircraft available for training, the basic structures and systems are common to all. To the fuselage are attached the engine, wings, tail and wheels. Sometimes the wings are mounted high as in the Cessna above, but they may be low as in the Piper, but you will also see other arrangements such as the biplane *(Tiger Moth)*. On the trailing edge and outboard, moveable surfaces known as the ailerons are fitted and inboard are the flaps. At the rear of the aeroplane is the tail section comprising a horizontal portion and a vertical portion. To each are attached moveable surfaces - the elevator to the horizontal tailplane surface and the rudder to the vertical fin. The tailplane may be an all-moving horizontal stabilator *(as in the Piper)* and it may also be mounted high in a "**T**" shape as in the Piper Tomahawk (PA38), although more conventionally it is arranged as in the photos.

The engine drives the propeller and this generates the thrust to pull the aircraft through the air. The effect of this is to create the aerodynamic force known as **LIFT**, which supports the aircraft in flight.

The cockpit may be entered through doors on either side, as in the Cessna or over the wing through a single door (PA28) or doors on either side (PA38). Usually the seating is arranged side by side and the convention is for the Commander to sit on the left, thus you, as the student will occupy the left-hand seat and the instructor the right-hand seat. Beneath the fuselage the undercarriage or landing gear is arranged, more usually in the "tricycle" configuration, but on older aircraft you will see the tailwheel configuration where the tailwheel replaces the nosewheel. The nosewheel is usually connected to the rudder pedals, situated on the floor of the cockpit. Movement of these pedals provides directional control to enable the aircraft to be steered on the ground. Brakes are operated by pressing the top portion of the rudder pedals or by using a handle in the cockpit.

AIRMANSHIP

The word airmanship is one of the most frequently used words in your flying training. It encompasses all aspects of safety, pilot awareness, rules and regulations and matters which differentiate the "good pilot" from the "poor pilot". In each lesson you will learn new aspects of airmanship in addition to the flying skills.

Quiz No 1.1

1. The wings, engine, tail and wheels are attached the .... of the aeroplane.

2. On the trailing edge and outboard of the wings, ... are attached.

3. The horizontal moving surface at the rear of the aeroplane is the ....

4. The vertical moving surface at the rear of the aeroplane is the ....

5. The undercarriage may be either .... or ....

6. Safety aspects, awareness, rules and regulations all form part of ....

Answers
No 1.1

1. Fuselage.
2. Ailerons.
3. Elevator.
4. Rudder.
5. Tricycle or Tailwheel.
6. Airmanship.

LESSON OBJECTIVE

By the end of the lesson you will be able to identify accurately the main instrumentation of your training aeroplane.

AIRMANSHIP

Pilot Knowledge.

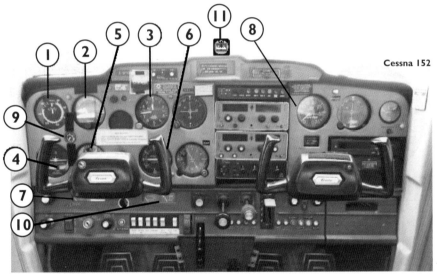

Cessna 152

1.	Airspeed Indicator	2.	Attitude Indicator	3.	Altimeter
4.	Slip Ball	5.	Heading Indicator	6.	Vertical Speed Indicator
7.	Fuel Gauges	8.	Tachometer	9.	Suction Gauge
10.	Oil Temperature & Pressure Gauges	11.	Magnetic Compass		

The Cockpit

The cockpit of the aeroplane contains all of the controls and instruments used to operate the aeroplane. You will need to understand each of the controls and instruments to be able to handle the aircraft safely in the air as well as on the ground. The instruments are divided into flight instruments and engine performance instruments.

They will be arranged slightly differently in each aeroplane and therefore it is very useful for you to spend a few minutes sitting in the aeroplane before the engine is running in order to familiarise yourself with the location and presentation of each instrument.

The Flight Instruments

The flight instruments include the airspeed indicator (**ASI**), the attitude indicator (**AI**) which shows the aircraft's attitude relative to the horizon, the altimeter to show altitude above sea level, a turn coordinator *(or turn indicator on older aircraft)* and balance ball, a direction indicator (**DI**) to complement the compass to show heading and a vertical speed indicator (**VSI**).

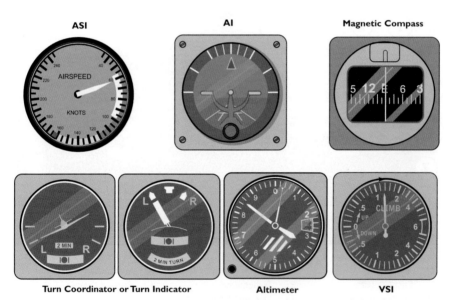

Air pressure is used to drive the ASI, VSI and altimeter and this is obtained through the pitot-static system. The information about attitude (**AI**), heading (**DI**) and turning *(turn coordinator)* is derived from gyroscopes, which may be air-driven or electrically spun. Thus there are instruments to provide information about the health of these systems - a suction gauge and ammeter. Some turn coordinators are fitted with red warning flags which show when the electrical source is off or if the instrument fails. Additionally a magnetic compass is provided usually positioned well above the instrument panel to prevent magnetic interference from the instruments and radios.

The Engine Performance Instruments

The engine instruments include the fuel gauges the tachometer *(which shows the engine rpm)*, oil temperature and pressure gauges and on low wing aeroplanes, a fuel pressure gauge. Other instruments may be included such as cylinder head temperature gauge, exhaust temperature gauge and even a carburettor ice indicator.

Quiz No 1.2

1. The Flight Instruments include the ....(ASI), ... (AI) and ....

2. Gyroscopes provide information about ....(AI), ...(DI) and .... (Turn Coordinator).

3. The health of the gyroscopic systems is shown by reference to the ...., ... and ....

4. Some Engine Instruments include .... and ....

Answers
No 1.2

1. Airspeed Indicator,
   Attitude Indicator,
   & Altimeter.
2. Attitude, Heading
   & Turning.
3. Suction Gauge,
   Ammeter,
   Red Warning Flags.
4. Tachometer,
   Oil Temperature
   & Pressure Gauges,
   Fuel Pressure Gauge.

1.3 LESSON AIM

To learn the main systems of the aeroplane.

LESSON OBJECTIVE

By the end of the lesson you will be able to identify and use the main systems of your training aeroplane with accuracy.

AIRMANSHIP

Pilot Knowledge.

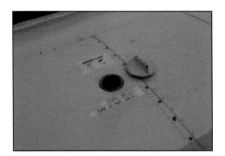

Fuel System

Fuel is fed through pipes or hoses from the fuel tanks to the carburettor. An engine-driven pump assists the process. In high wing aircraft the fuel is fed by "gravity feed" but in low wing aircraft it is necessary to have an auxiliary fuel pump to assist the fuel flow. There will be a fuel selector valve installed in the cockpit. This has two purposes - to enable the pilot to turn off the fuel in the event of a fire - and to enable selection of one or other or both tanks depending on the arrangement adopted by the particular aeroplane.

Fuel gauges are fitted in the cockpit to assist the pilot to ascertain the amount of fuel in the tanks, but since these are notoriously inaccurate it is essential to inspect visually the contents of the tanks before flight. Drain plugs are also fitted and you should always strain a small amount of fuel into a clear container to inspect for water or impurities as part of your preflight checks. A primer is often fitted to assist with starting the engine. You will need to read the Pilot's Operating Handbook for your aircraft to ascertain the fuel capacity and the consumption rates in addition to familiarising yourself with the details of the system in use.

Piper PA38

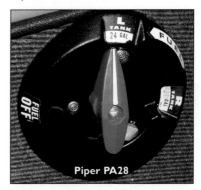
Piper PA28

Ignition System

The engine ignition system is provided by two magnetos which are attached to the engine and are separate from the aircraft's electrical system. Each cylinder has two spark plugs and separate ignition leads, thus one system will provide a back up for the other if it fails. In the cockpit, there is generally a switch operated by a key, which has five positions, OFF, RIGHT, LEFT, BOTH and START. In order to check that the starter motor has disengaged after start there is a red warning light provided.

Cessna

Piper

Electrical System

This includes the Red Master Switch with which the battery is selected on. Depending on the aircraft type there will be fuses or circuit breakers, an alternator switch (which may be part of the battery master switch as page 24). A low voltage warning light is also required in the UK.

Lubrication System

The engine oil is generally stored in a small sump at the bottom of the crankcase. There is an oil filler pipe, which is accessible through the front engine cowling via an access hatch. You should always check the oil quantity before flight by removing the dipstick, which will be marked with levels. Oil comes in several grades and you will need to check that you have put in the correct type for your engine, as the usage varies according to many factors *(read more about this in Volume 4)*. There are two gauges in the cockpit to inform you of the temperature and pressure of the oil, vital information for the pilot as to the condition of the engine.

Other Equipment

There may be a first aid kit and fire extinguisher supplied. You should check these for serviceability and security. A control lock may have been inserted to prevent damage to the controls of the aircraft and this must be removed before carrying out your walkaround inspection of the aircraft. A pitot cover may have been placed over the pitot head to protect it from blockage by insects or water. Again this needs to be removed and stowed. Chocks or tie downs may be in place and these should be removed and stowed carefully to prevent other aircraft from taxying over them and causing damage.

$\mathcal{Q}uiz$ No 1.3

1. In low wing aeroplanes a .... is required to assist fuel flow.

2. The .... is used to switch on the battery.

3. Two .... provide the engine ignition system.

4. The .... and .... gauges in the cockpit provide information about the engine oil.

5. Equipment to protect the aeroplane which should be removed before flight includes ...., ... and .... or ....

Answers

No 1.3

1. Fuel Pump.
2. Master Switch.
3. Magnetos.
4. Temperature,
   Pressure.
5. Control Locks,
   Pitot Covers,
   Chocks, Tie Downs.

1.4 LESSON AIM

To learn how to use the aeroplane checklists, drills and controls.

LESSON OBJECTIVE

By the end of the lesson you will be able to use the aeroplane checklists accurately and demonstrate the associated drills. You will be able to identify the main controls of your training aeroplane and demonstrate their use.

AIRMANSHIP

Pilot Knowledge.

Checklist

Checklists are used to organise the order in which checks are carried out and to reduce the possibility of omissions which may occur if you rely on your memory. Checklists should be used when you fly infrequently or often fly different types of aircraft. Additionally it is helpful to use them for the start-up checks, after start checks, power checks and pre-takeoff checks.

However, certain drills and checks need to be committed to memory, notably the pre-landing checks and the immediate actions to take in the unlikely event of in-flight emergency. After the initial emergency drills have been carried out you should still refer to a checklist to ensure that nothing has been missed.

Control Column

In your training aeroplane it is likely that you will have a control yoke but you may have a control column *(see page 27)*. Forward and backward movement of the yoke or column moves the elevator up and down. Sideways movement of the column or rotational control movement of the yoke operates the ailerons.

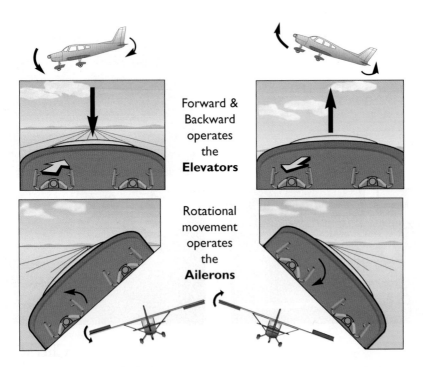

Forward &
Backward
operates
the
Elevators

Rotational
movement
operates
the
Ailerons

Rudder & Brakes

The use of these has already been described above. The toe brakes should not generally be operated whilst taxying the aircraft other than to provide assistance in turning. However, from time to time it may be necessary to apply the brakes to slow down when taxying on a hard surface. The handbrake is only used for parking.

Handbrake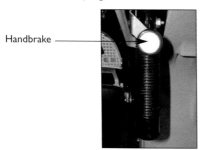

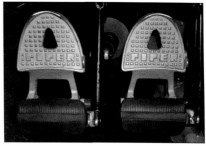

Mixture, Throttle & Carburettor Heat

These controls may be of a push/pull type or set on a quadrant. In all cases the pushing in or up of the throttle will increase the power, pulling out or down will reduce the power. Pushing the mixture lever in or up will enrichen the mixture, whilst pulling the lever out or down will lean the mixture and eventually stop it running by starving the carburettor of fuel. The correct use of mixture is dealt with in Chapter 4. The operation of the carburettor heat control is also dealt with in Chapter 4, but basically the control is used to direct hot air into the carburettor intake to prevent ice from forming and blocking the intake even on a warm day. The design of a carburettor means that this problem may occur in conditions of high relative humidity or when there is a low power setting, so its use is a safety factor.

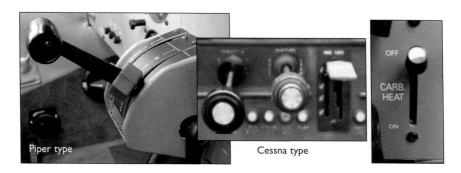

Piper type   Cessna type

Flaps

The flaps are fitted to the trailing edge of the wings and are used to steepen the aircraft's approach path by creating extra drag which also enables a slower safe approach speed to be used. This also improves forward visibility and reduces the take-off and landing roll. In some aircraft the flaps are operated manually by a lever. In others they may be operated electrically and there may be an indicator fitted to show you how many degrees of flap you have selected. You should check the operation of the flaps before flight.

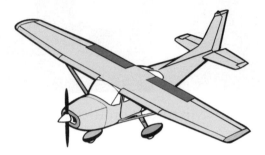

Trim Control

Aircraft are all fitted with a trim control linked to the elevator or stabilator. Some aircraft also have rudder trimmers fitted. The purpose of this is to relieve the control column load experienced by the pilot and thus to assist in smooth flying. A wheel or lever is fitted to the cockpit connected by cables to the trim tab. You should check the operation of this wheel on the ground.

PA38 Piper Tomahawk Elevator Trimwheel

PA28 Rudder Trimwheel

There are many different types of radios and intercom systems and your instructor will show you how to use the equipment fitted in your training aeroplane. Some aeroplanes may have more than one radio set fitted, as well as various radio navigation installations. You will learn more about the latter later in your training *(see Chapter 18c)*. For more information on Radio Communications see Volume 5 of this series.

Quiz No 1.4

1.   A Checklist should be used to ....

2.   The Control used to increase or reduce power is the ....

3.   Pulling out or closing the mixture lever will .... the engine.

4.   Use of the .... will help prevent ice forming and blocking the ....

5.   Another moving surface fitted to the trailing edge of the wings (inboard) is the ....

6.   To relieve control loads a .... is fitted.

Answers
No 1.4

1. Reduce the possibility of Omissions.
2. Throttle.
3. Stop.
4. Carburettor Heat, Intake.
5. Flaps.
6. Trimwheel.

1E. LESSON AIM

To learn the emergency fire drills.

LESSON OBJECTIVE

By the end of the lesson you will be able to state accurately the procedures for:

- Engine fire on start up
- Engine fire in flight
- Electrical fire on the ground
- Electrical fire in flight
- Cabin fire during flight
- Emergency escape procedures
- Operation of fire extinguishers

AIRMANSHIP

Pilot Knowledge.

Fuel   The Triangle of Fire   Heat

Oxygen

The emergency drills and procedures are not set out in detail here, as they will vary with each aircraft type. You should refer to the Pilot's Operating Handbook (**POH**) or specific aircraft manual for further details. Your instructor will point out to you the relevant drills to learn.

Exercise 1E   Emergency Drills

AIR EXERCISE   *Not Applicable*

Teaching Points

1. **Engine Fire on Start Up***
    a)   Keep the engine turning with the starter and at the same time put mixture into idle cut off.
    b)   Fuel off.
    c)   Magnetos off.
    d)   Inform ATC.
    e)   Master switch off.
    f)   Evacuate the aircraft taking the fire extinguisher with you.

2. **Engine Fire during Flight***
    a)   Mixture control to idle cut off.
    b)   Throttle closed.
    c)   Magnetos off.
    d)   Fuel off.
    e)   Cabin heater off.
    f)   Send out a **MAYDAY** call and carry out a forced landing.

3. **Electrical Fire on the Ground**
    a)   Shut down the engine.
    b)   Inform ATC.
    c)   Master switch off.
    d)   Evacuate the aircraft taking the fire extinguisher with you.

4. Electrical Fire during Flight
a) Inform ATC.
b) Master switch off.
c) Cabin heater off.
d) Use the fire extinguisher as required and open the fresh air vents.
e) Land at the nearest aerodrome.

5. Cabin Fire during Flight
a) Use the fire extinguisher as required and open the fresh air vent.
b) Inform ATC.
c) Land as soon as possible.

* **Precise order of actions should be in accordance with aircraft checklist.**

These exercises will be practised at appropriate points of the syllabus.

Exercise 1E

LESSON AIM

To learn the action in the event of a systems failure.

LESSON OBJECTIVE

By the end of the lesson you will be able to state the procedure accurately to deal with these types of systems failure.

AIRMANSHIP

Thorough Pre-flight with Checklist. Knowledge of Aircraft Systems. Knowledge of Emergency Drills. Aircraft Manual.

AIR EXERCISE   *Not Applicable*

Teaching Points

1.	Water in fuel - checks and drain.
2.	Fuse/circuit breakers.
3.	Leaking fuel/oil.
4.	Oil pressure and oil temperature.
5.	Fuel pressure.
6.	Flat battery.
7.	Ammeter/low voltage light.
8.	Vacuum system.

Exercise 1E Emergency Drills

LESSON AIM

To learn the Escape Drills, Location and use of Emergency Equipment and Exits.

LESSON OBJECTIVE

By the end of the lesson you will be able to state the Escape Drills, locate and use the aeroplane's Emergency Exits and Equipment carried.

AIRMANSHIP

Thorough Pre-flight. Knowledge of Aircraft Systems. Knowledge of relevant Emergency Drills. Knowledge of the aeroplane's Emergency Equipment.

AIR EXERCISE   *Not Applicable*

Teaching Points

1. Life Jackets if required.

2. Fire Extinguisher type and in date.

3. Escape routes/hatches.

4. First Aid Equipment and in date.

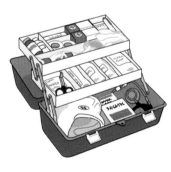

Left Intentionally Blank

Chapter 2

Preparation for and Action after Flight

---

2. LESSON AIM

To learn the actions that are required to prepare yourself and the aeroplane for flight and the actions required after flight.

LESSON OBJECTIVE

By the end of the lesson you will be able to state and demonstrate the procedures to prepare yourself and the aeroplane for flight, state and demonstrate the procedures after flight.

AIRMANSHIP

Airfield procedures. Checklist. Aeroplane documentation. Mass & Balance. ATC Liaison.

Personal Preparation

Your Fitness to Fly

You need to consider a number of factors. If you have consumed any alcohol in the previous eight hours or taken any kind of medication, drugs or pills which could impair your abilities you should not fly. If you have a cold or upper respiratory complaint you should not fly as you may damage your ears. Consider if you are stressed by outside factors or by arriving late, are you fatigued and have you eaten recently? If in doubt it is best to stay on the ground. Problems which may seem minor on the ground may be magnified in the air.

Your Clothing

Wear comfortable non-restricting clothing, preferably made of natural fibres. It can be windy at the airfield so take a jacket or pullover for the walkaround which you can remove for the flight. If you are too hot it may result in queasiness. Shoes should be non-slip and the soles should not be too thick. High heels are definitely unsuitable.

Your Equipment

Do you have all the charts, navigational equipment, headsets etc required for the flight?

Pre-flight Documentation

The Aircraft Documents

You will need to check the service record of the aeroplane and its airworthiness certificate, as well as insurance certificate. Additionally you will check the technical log and deferred defects schedule and weight and balance schedule. Further details of this are set out in the chapter on airworthiness in Volume 2.

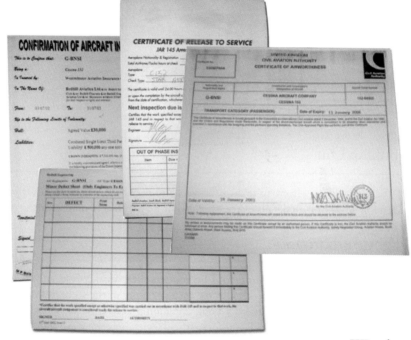

Weather

The weather is a consideration of every flight and you should check the up to date forecast or discuss it with your instructor before every flight. You may need to check the NOTAMS and navigational warnings and compile a flight log before the flight. Further details on this are in Chapter 18, Navigation.

Weight & Balance

No flight must take place if the weight limit of the aeroplane is exceeded. The load must also be arranged within the centre of gravity limits. Most training aircraft will not exceed the weight and balance and centre of gravity limits with two average-sized people on board, so you will not have to prepare this schedule every flight, but it is a good habit to get into and if either you or your instructor is particularly heavy you may not be able to take full fuel in your two-seater training aeroplane.

Booking Out

This will vary from airfield to airfield. You may have to telephone air traffic control in advance with details of your flight or it may suffice to do it over the radio.

Flight Authorisation

Each flight has to be authorised by your training organisation and this may be recorded on a separate sheet or effected by a signature in the technical log of the aeroplane. There will probably be a book containing "Flying Orders" i.e. specific rules relating to your school and/or airfield with which you will need to familiarise yourself.

Aircraft Preparation

External Inspection

Your checklist will detail the precise items to be inspected, but some items are common to all aircraft. As you walk towards the aircraft you should look at the position of it as some things may not be apparent when you are close up - i.e. whether it is sitting too much tail down or up, or one wing low. You should also note how it is parked to ensure there are no obstacles to taxying, and that the ground surface is suitable for taxying.

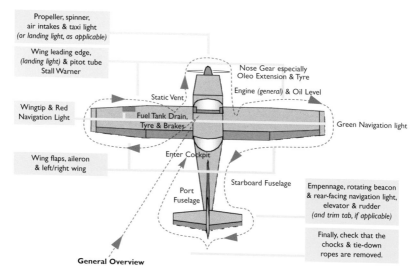

Propeller, spinner, air intakes & taxi light *(or landing light, as applicable)*

Wing leading edge, *(landing light)* & pitot tube Stall Warner

Nose Gear especially Oleo Extension & Tyre

Engine *(general)* & Oil Level

Static Vent

Wingtip & Red Navigation Light

Fuel Tank Drain, Tyre & Brakes

Green Navigation light

Wing flaps, aileron & left/right wing

Enter Cockpit

Starboard Fuselage

Port Fuselage

Empennage, rotating beacon & rear-facing navigation light, elevator & rudder *(and trim tab, if applicable)*

Finally, check that the chocks & tie-down ropes are removed.

General Overview

Start by removing all chocks, tie-downs, control locks and stow them safely. Check for any unusual dents, scratches, buckling or stressing of the skin, popped rivets etc. Look for any signs of leaking fuel, oil or hydraulic fluids. Gently move all of the control surfaces fully against their stops to check that there is nothing snagging. Your instructor will show you how to check for security of linkages.

Check the fuel contents for quantity and also take samples to check for impurities. Check the oil quantity.

Inspect the undercarriage legs and wheels and tyres. Look at the brakes to check there are no hydraulic leaks and the pads and discs are secure. Check the tyres for inflation, cuts, and creep *(against the painted marks)*. The nose oleo should be checked for correct extension and to ensure there is no leaking of oil from the seals.

All vents and inlets should be clear. All inspection panels should be in place. Make sure that the windscreen and other windows are clean and free of cracks.

If you are in any doubt about anything then you should ask your instructor or an engineer. With practice you will learn to recognise things that do not look right.

Internal Inspection

This should include:

- confirming that the brakes are on
- adjusting the seat and harness position to fit you correctly
- checking the fuel is ON
- checking that the magnetos are OFF
- checking full and free and correct movement of the controls including the trim wheels and flaps
- checking engine controls for full and free movement
- no fuses or circuit breakers popped
- headsets plugged in
- luggage safely stowed
- any necessary charts and navigational equipment easily to hand
- checklists available
- safety equipment in place

Engine Start-up

Having checked that the aeroplane is in a position suitable for start-up, i.e. well away from buildings, people, loose stones or gravel, follow the checklist for the start-up procedures then place your feet on the brakes, open the window and immediately shout out "**Clear Prop**" before cranking the starter. Once the engine has started then release the starter and check that the red warning light has gone out. Further checks after start will be required *(use the checklist)* including monitoring the oil pressure, ammeter and suction gauge. You will set a low rpm, usually 1200, to allow a gentle warm-up period for the engine. Next you will check each magneto in turn to ensure that the engine does not stop. You will see a small drop in rpm as you switch off one magneto and this should increase again to the previous value when you switch back to both.

Problems on Start-up

*Flooded engine: You may inadvertently "**flood**" the engine by over-priming. If this is suspected, switch off the magnetos, open the throttle fully, ensure the fuel is switched on, then set the mixture to idle cut off. Crank the engine several times which will clear the excess fuel through the intake and then repeat the starting procedure without priming. This is a general procedure, but different aircraft may differ slightly, so consult the checklist for your aircraft type. Engine fire on start up: see Chapter 1E.*

Prior to taxying, the DI should be aligned with the magnetic compass. The radio should be switched on, the squelch and volume adjusted and the intercom checked. After the appropriate clearance has been obtained from air traffic, then the aircraft will be taxied to the holding point. Before starting to taxy the aircraft close the throttle and release the brakes. Then once clear of the parking area close the throttle and test the brakes on each side to ensure that they are working symmetrically. Taxying checks will be carried out as detailed in Chapter 5.

Engine Power Checks

At the holding point, the aircraft will be manoeuvred to face into wind and well clear of stones or gravel. Ensure that there is no aircraft or other object or person behind you which could be damaged by your propeller slipstream. Apply the brakes and then, referring to the checklist carry out the items listed for the Power checks. Typically this will involve increasing the rpm to between 1700 and 2000, checking there is no carburettor ice present, then switching off each magneto in turn to check that each ignition system is functioning properly. The maximum and minimum figures permitted for the drop in rpm will be indicated on the checklist for your aircraft. The engine gauges, suction and vacuum must be checked for steady readings and then the throttle should be closed to check the idling rpm, normally between 500 and 700.

The Pre-Takeoff (Vital) Actions

These are also listed on the checklist. See further, Chapter 12.

Engine Shut-down Procedures

After the flight it is important to carry out the correct running down and shut down procedures for the aeroplane and again these will be listed in the checklist. The engine needs a little time to cool down before being switched off and ideally this will occur as you taxy back to the parking area or hangar, at a relatively low rpm (1200). You should park the aircraft facing into wind wherever possible then apply the parking brake. Follow the proper shutdown procedure which will always include a further magneto check. This is for safety reasons since it is possible that an earthing wire may have become detached during flight which would leave the danger of a "**live**" magneto. This would mean that although the magneto had apparently been turned off with the key, it would in fact still be "**on**". Turning the propeller in this condition would be very dangerous as the engine could start up and the propeller could then cause injury. Therefore each magneto should be switched off in turn to check that a drop of rpm is shown. After this check the engine will be stopped by moving the mixture lever to the "**idle cut-off**" position. Then the switches should all be turned off and keys removed from the magneto switch.

The control lock should be put in place and the pitot cover fitted. After leaving the aircraft, ensure that the harnesses are left tidy for the next user. If necessary, chock or tie down the aircraft. It is your responsibility as pilot to ensure the security of the aircraft.

Post-flight Documentation

You may need to "**book in**" with air traffic. Complete the authorisation sheet and the technical log, recording any defects which may have arisen during the flight. Report these to an instructor or engineer. Then you should complete your personal logbook with the details of the flight and the exercises carried out.

Quiz No. 2

1. List factors affecting your fitness to fly.

2. Which aircraft documents need to be checked before flight?

3. Procedures to be completed before flight include
............, ..., ..., ... and ....

4. What precautions should you take before starting the engine?

5. At the holding point .... checks are carried out.

6. After flight .... procedures, as listed on the ....
should be carried out.

Answers No. 2

1. Alcohol, Medication, Drugs, Headcolds, Stress, Fatigue, Food.
2. Service Record, Airworthiness Certificate, Insurance,
   Technical Log, Deferred Defects Schedule,
   Weight and Balance Schedule.
3. Booking out, Flight Authorisation, External Inspection,
   Internal Inspection.
4. It is in a suitable position, away from buildings, loose stones
   or gravel, ensure the brakes are on.
5. Engine Power.
6. Engine Shut-down, Checklist.

Chapter 3

Air Experience

LESSON AIM

>To give you the opportunity to get the feel of being airborne in a light aeroplane and to experience the sensations of flying an aeroplane.

LESSON OBJECTIVE

>By the end of the lesson you will be able to make a judgment whether to continue to learn to fly or not.

AIRMANSHIP

>Airfield safety procedures. Sitting comfortably. Strap-in correctly. Reaching controls. Handing and taking over control. Following through on controls. LOOKOUT.

Your First Flight

If you have never been in a light aeroplane before then this is your chance to experience what it is like to be airborne. Although this is not a formal lesson, you will be able to handle the controls and this will give you a feel for what flying is about. You will also feel the sensations of flying the aeroplane. Before the flight your instructor will give you a briefing on safety matters (**"airmanship"**) and explain such matters as where you will fly and what you will be able to do.

In the Cockpit

The instructor will assist you to adjust your seat and the harness to ensure that you are comfortable as you will otherwise become distracted and will not learn. Try to relax even if you are nervous. There are fresh air vents which may be positioned to make you more comfortable.

It is important that you can hear what the instructor is saying, so ensure that the headset is adjusted correctly and the intercom is working.

You will notice the duplicated controls. The instructor will show you how to place your hands on the control wheel and feet on the rudder pedals, in order to **"follow-through"** to feel the movements he is making.

Once Airborne

After take-off the aircraft will climb away to leave the busy circuit area around the airfield. You will notice the changing perspective of the ground features as you gain altitude. Try to keep your gaze outside the aircraft as this is a good habit to develop right from the start. In flight the instructor will allow you to follow through and then he will hand you control to experience flying the aircraft. In order to do this he will say **"you have control"** and you should then place your hand lightly on the control yoke *(or column)* and your feet on the rudder pedals. Once you are ready you should say **"I have control"** and the instructor will release control to you. When he requires to take back control he will say **"I have control"** and you should acknowledge, **"You have control"** then he will take the controls and you should release them. This is very important as it ensures that you both know who is flying the aeroplane and you will not be opposing each other for control, which could be dangerous.

During the flight it is necessary to keep a good lookout for other aircraft and to remain aware of the surroundings in order to navigate and to avoid flying into clouds or obstructions. It is usual in visual flying to relate the position of the nose of the aircraft to the horizon; this is known as the "**normal attitude**" and will be referred to in later chapters. As there are plenty of blind spots caused by the aircraft's structure it is necessary to make turns from time to time to check the areas ahead. You will be taught how to describe the position of another aircraft in relation to your own using the "**clock code**" *(more about this in Chapter 4).*

The Landing

During the return to the airfield and preparation for landing, your instructor will have to make various radio calls and carry out pre-landing checks. The landing phase will seem very busy and your instructor may not be able to explain everything that is happening as it is all over very quickly. After the aircraft has been taxied back to the parking area various administrative procedures will have to be completed. You may well be full of questions which your instructor will be pleased to answer. As your first flight is now over and the wonderful new world of flying opens up to you, you will be filled with enthusiasm. In order to ensure that you derive the maximum benefit from your next lesson, it is helpful to read ahead in the manual and your instructor will guide you as to the appropriate sections to prepare. In addition you will have a syllabus which will assist you to monitor your progress through the course.

Left Intentionally Blank

Chapter 4

The Primary and Secondary Effects of the Main Flying Controls

During your flying training you will gradually be introduced to the concept of airmanship. You should develop good habits early and thus it is important to use the correct **"You have control"** - **"I have control"** procedures at all times to be sure who has the control of the aircraft. Hold the controls lightly and move them smoothly applying gentle control pressures rather than abrupt movements.

Try to look out of the cockpit most of the time to check for other aircraft as well as to note the position of the aircraft relative to the horizon. Use the **Clock Code** to identify the position of other aircraft. *(shown below)*

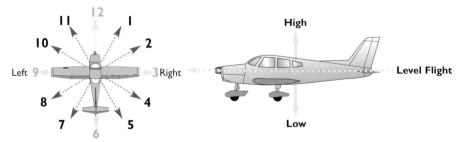

Example: Left 10 o'clock High

Introduction

An aircraft's movement is described with reference to three reference axes which are at 90° to each other. The diagram below and the table underneath will clarify this for you.

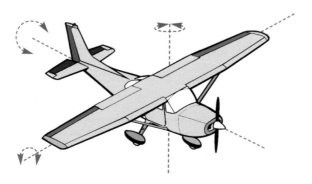

The Main Controls and Planes and Axes of Movement			
Plane of Movement	Control Surface	Cockpit Control Surface	Axis
PITCH	Elevators	Control Column Forward & Back	Lateral
ROLL	Ailerons	Control Column Left & Right	Longitudinal
YAW	Rudders	Rudder Pedals Left & Right	Normal

Motion of the aircraft will occur in all three planes of movement: this is relative to the aircraft itself, not to the horizon. However, the horizon will be your primary reference to enable you to select a particular attitude with one or more of the main controls.

Whilst an aircraft can be moved in any of the three planes shown above, its design will incorporate a degree of stability. This means that if the aircraft is disturbed from its flight path by a gust of wind, it will have a natural ability to return to that path without any input from the pilot. Training aeroplanes tend to be very stable in pitch and yaw and if correctly trimmed *(see next section)* will maintain flight in a steady path with "**hands off**".

In the rolling plane most aircraft tend to be less stable. Thus a disturbance of the wings can lead to a spiral descent if the pilot does not correct this by levelling the wings.

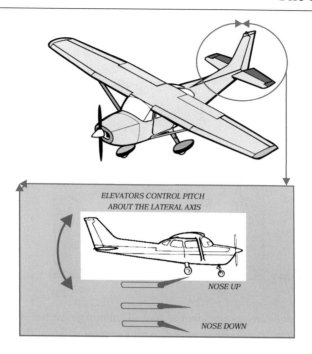

ELEVATORS CONTROL PITCH
ABOUT THE LATERAL AXIS

NOSE UP

NOSE DOWN

The elevator *(or stabilator on aircraft with an all-flying tailplane)* is operated by fore and aft movements of the control wheel and controls the pitching movement of the aircraft. As the control wheel is moved backwards, the hinged surface at the rear of the tailplane is moved up changing the airflow around the tail. The air underneath the tailplane will speed up and reduce the static pressure resulting in a down force. This causes the aircraft to rotate about its longitudinal axis and the nose pitches up. This will continue whilst the backpressure on the control wheel is applied. When the control wheel is set in the neutral position, the new high nose attitude will be held. Larger pitch movements will result in an increased rate of movement.

To return the aircraft to the normal attitude, it is necessary to apply forward pressure to move the control wheel forwards. As the control wheel is moved forwards, the elevator *(or stabilator)* will move down, creating an upwards lift force at the tail. Now the aircraft will rotate forwards, pitching nose down and will continue to do so until the control wheel is once again returned to the neutral control position. The required attitude can be selected and held.

The Ailerons

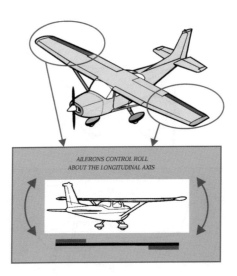

AILERONS CONTROL ROLL
ABOUT THE LONGITUDINAL AXIS

The ailerons are operated by the control column or control wheel and these control the aircraft in roll. In an aircraft with a control column, the movement is left/right. In aircraft with a control wheel the movement is a rotation left or right. As one aileron goes down, the other goes up. The downward movement of an aileron increases the lift generated by that wing, whilst the upward movement reduces the lift over that wing causing an imbalance which results in the roll towards the upgoing aileron. The aircraft will continue to roll until the control column is centralised when an angle of bank will be held. To return the aircraft to the normal attitude it is necessary to apply aileron in the opposite direction which effectively reverses the imbalance of lift over the wings.

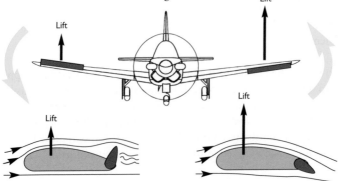

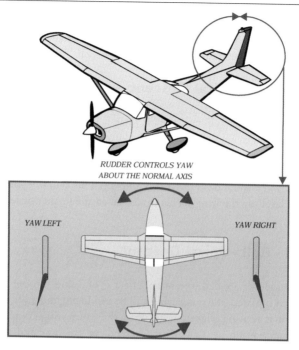

RUDDER CONTROLS YAW
ABOUT THE NORMAL AXIS

YAW LEFT   *YAW RIGHT*

The rudder pedals situated on the floor operate the rudders. The pedals are interconnected so that one moves back when the other moves forwards. Pressing the left rudder pedal causes the rudder surface, hinged on the vertical fin, to pivot towards the left. This accelerates the airflow on the right side of the fin, producing a force in that area. This leads to a rotation of the aircraft about the normal axis yawing the nose of the aircraft to the left. Conversely, pressing the right pedal will yaw the aircraft to the right.

This action of deliberately yawing the aircraft about the normal axis is uncomfortable and is inefficient as a method of turning the aircraft as the amount of drag increases. The main purpose of the rudder is not to create yaw deliberately but to prevent unwanted yaw. This is often referred to as **"maintaining balance"** or **"balanced flight"**. The pilot will feel the aircraft being out of balance as there will be a sensation of leaning towards one side or the other. The balance ball on the instrument panel will also show if you are out of balance or not and you can use this indication to correct the condition. If the ball is out to the right then centre it with a little right rudder pressure and vice versa.

The Further Effects of the Main Controls

There is an inter-relationship between the operations of the aileron and the rudder, whereby the secondary effect of movement of the ailerons creates yaw and the secondary effect of the rudder movement creates roll.

Roll - Slip - Yaw - Spiral Descent

When you bank the aircraft, the lift force is inclined and a sideways force is created. This will lead to a sideslip towards the lower wing. As a result, the large areas of keel and fin surface will be struck by the airflow. Since these are behind the centre of gravity the aircraft will start to yaw in the direction of the sideslip and then the nose will lower and a spiral descent will commence. This can, of course be prevented by the pilot levelling the wings. This yaw is called the further or secondary effect of ailerons.

Yaw - Skid - Roll - Spiral Descent

When rudder is applied, the initial effect is of a skid through the air. Once the yaw has been initiated, the outer wing will be producing more lift than the inner wing, because it is moving slightly faster than the inner wing compared with the relative airflow. A portion of the wing is "masked" by the nose and fuselage of the aircraft. This imbalance in lift will lead to a roll in the same direction as the yaw, even though there is no aileron applied. If left uncorrected, once again a spiral descent will follow. Thus roll is the further or secondary effect of yaw.

Effect of Airspeed

Effectiveness of the flying controls depends on the speed of airflow passing over the control surfaces. At a higher airspeed the controls are very effective and only a very small movement is required to achieve the desired affect. Conversely at slow airspeeds, the controls are less effective and larger movements are required. To see this, you will select a lower nose attitude and trim for a faster airspeed. You will feel the controls become much firmer and more responsive. Then you will pitch up and trim for a nose up attitude. The airspeed will reduce and you will feel the controls become much 'sloppier' and less responsive.

Effect of Slipstream

The slipstream generated from the propeller spirals back around the fuselage of the aeroplane increasing the airflow over the tailplane making the rudder and elevator more effective. The ailerons are outside the slipstream airflow and are therefore not influenced by the slipstream effect. On a T-tailed aircraft the elevator will also be less affected as it will tend to be above the influence of the slipstream.

The other effect of the slipstream is to produce a horizontal aerodynamic force or sideways component which impinges the fin and rear fuselage more on one side than the other which tends to yaw the tail. This effect varies with both rpm and airspeed. The lower the airspeed then the tighter the coils of the spiral increasing the angle of attack relative to the fin. This causes an increase in the yaw effect. At higher airspeeds the angle of attack reduces, there is a smaller horizontal lift force and the yaw is less. The direction of the yaw will depend on the direction of rotation of the propeller. If it rotates clockwise *(as seen from the cockpit)*, the nose will yaw left and can be balanced with right rudder. It will be most pronounced at high power and low airspeed combinations as in a climb. Some aircraft have an offset fin to overcome this effect at cruising power.

Effect of Power

Opening the throttle, or increasing power causes the propeller to rotate faster and generate increased thrust. Closing the throttle reduces power. These movements should be made smoothly. In addition to the increase in slipstream and increasing the yaw, an increase in power will cause a pitch up to occur. A forward pressure on the control column can counteract this. Reducing power will cause a pitch down which again can be counteracted by backpressure on the control column. The yawing effects in both cases can be counteracted by applying rudder pressure.

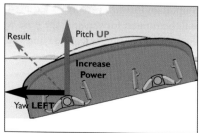

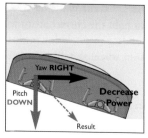

Effect of Trimming

The trimming controls are provided to assist the pilot by relieving the control loads experienced in flight. Your training aeroplane will have an elevator trimmer and some aircraft will also be fitted with trim controls on the rudder to relieve steady pressures on the rudder pedals. A small control surface *(tab)* will be located on the trailing edge of the elevator and it will be operated by a wheel in the cockpit.

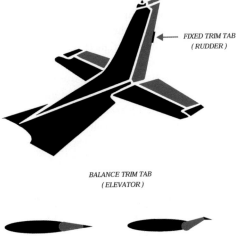

FIXED TRIM TAB
(RUDDER)

BALANCE TRIM TAB
(ELEVATOR)

WARNING! TRIMMING CONTROLS ARE POWERFUL & SENSITIVE. MISHANDLING CAN CAUSE LOSS OF AIRCRAFT PERFORMANCE & UNDUE STRESS IN THE AIRFRAME.

Holding a control force or pressure for a sustained period of time would become tiring, therefore the trimmer can be used to hold a desired attitude. The correct way to use the trimmer is to select the desired attitude first and then wind the trim wheel to remove all of the pressure. Trim coarsely first, then fine trim by holding the control column very lightly. Trimming controls should not be used to relieve control loads of a transient nature such as during a turn. Correct use of the trimmer will make your flying easier and more accurate.

If the tendency of the aircraft is to pitch up, then forward pressure is required to hold the correct attitude, so the trimwheel will be rotated forwards. If the nose is tending to pitch down, then backpressure on the control column is required and the trim wheel should be rotated backwards.

Retrim the aircraft after each change of pitch attitude, each power change and each change of configuration *(flap selection)*.

Effect of Flaps

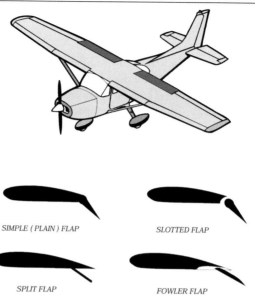

SIMPLE (PLAIN) FLAP   SLOTTED FLAP

SPLIT FLAP   FOWLER FLAP

There are many types of flaps used on aircraft but their basic purpose is the same. They are designed to vary the lift and/or drag. By increasing the lift the flaps reduce the stall speed and enable the aircraft to fly safely at lower airspeeds, which is particularly important on the approach to land. By increasing the drag, the flaps increase the steepness of the approach path and this improves the forward view which also assists the landing.

Flaps also reduce the touchdown speed thereby reducing the landing roll. Flaps also reduce the take-off roll. Flaps are usually fitted to the trailing edge of the wings, inboard (*i.e. next to the fuselage*). They are either operated electrically *(by a switch in the cockpit)* or mechanically by a handle or lever.

When flaps are operated they effectively change the shape of the wing and this alters the airflow over the wing, moving the centre of pressure and altering the angle of downwash over the tailplane. These factors all produce an increase in drag and a tendency for the aircraft to pitch when flap is selected. Thus the pilot will need to counteract the pitching tendency when selecting flap. When retracting flap the aircraft may sink and this again can be counteracted by backpressure on the control column. It is safest to raise or lower flaps in stages, trimming between each stage.

The design of the flaps will require that the flaps only operate within a certain airspeed range. This maximum speed is known as V_{FE}. The figure can be found in the Pilot's Operating Manual. The flaps should not be lowered above this speed nor should they be raised when the airspeed is below the "**clean stall speed**" (**V_{S1}**) *(see Chapter 10 for explanation)*.

Ancillary Controls

Carburettor Heat

The purpose of the carburettor heat is to prevent the formation of ice in the carburettor system and to remove it if it does form. The reason that this can occur is that the vapourisation of fuel causes cooling in the carburettor which may reduce the temperature below freezing. Additionally pressure reduction also leads to lowering of temperature *(Gas Laws)*. If the air contains sufficient water vapour, there may be ice formed in the induction system which can lead to blocking of the intake and stoppage of the engine. This can occur at temperatures of up to 27 degrees C. The carburettor heat control is usually a knob situated near the throttle and it is used to direct hot air into the carburettor intake. When hot air is applied there will be a drop in rpm and possibly some rough running, as the hot air is less dense than cold air. If ice is present, then there will be a rise in rpm as the ice melts.

On the ground hot air should not be selected for any length of time, as the hot air is unfiltered and there would be a risk of ingesting dirt, dust or grit which would damage the engine by abrasion.

In any operation at low power setting, full hot carburettor heat should be applied. This is usual in a descent. There should also be a periodic check every ten minutes or so by selecting heat for 10 seconds or so and then returning the knob to off *(cold)*.

Mixture Control

The mixture control is usually a red knob or lever, situated next to the throttle (see photo page 8). It is used to select the correct mixture for fuel economy and engine performance and to cut off the fuel to the engine to stop the engine at the end of a flight. At altitude the air density is less and therefore the amount of air being mixed with the fuel reduces with altitude. This is wasteful as the extra fuel will not be burnt but simply expelled in the exhaust gases. To select the correct mixture for the altitude the mixture lever should be moved out partly until the engine rpm shows a slight increase. If the mixture is moved further out past this peak the engine will start to run roughly and the rpm will reduce. Moving the mixture control slightly in towards the rich side will cause the engine to run smoothly and it is better to set the mixture slightly richer than too lean which could damage the engine by causing it to run too hot. It may also cause a condition known as detonation.

Stopping the engine by moving the mixture lever to the idle cut-off position is the optimum method, (rather than simply turning off the magneto switches) as it ensures that there is no unburnt fuel left in the cylinders or carburettor.

Environmental Controls

As it is essential that you are comfortable in the cockpit in order to maximise your ability to learn, it is necessary to understand the heating and ventilation system of your aircraft. It is unlikely that any air conditioning system is fitted, although some light aircraft will have a cooling fan. The heating is usually supplied by routing hot air from around the exhaust muffler. The problem is that if there is any cracking or leaking in the exhaust system then fumes and dangerous carbon monoxide could enter the cockpit without your knowledge. Carbon monoxide is poisonous and odourless thus its presence is not easily detected. Therefore you should always select fresh air at the same time as selecting heat in order to help prevent incapacitation.

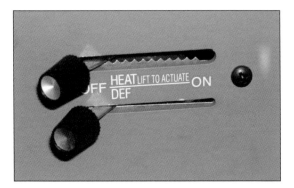

Other Controls

Depending on the aircraft type that you are flying, there will be other ancillary controls such as alternate static, alternate air *(if your engine is fuel injected)* and propeller levers *(if your propeller is of the variable pitch variety)*. Your instructor will advise you of these items and you should also study the Pilot's Operating Handbook to find out as much as possible about the operation of anything which is non-standard.

Left Intentionally Blank

Quiz No. 4

1. The Elevator is used to .... the aircraft in the .... axis.

2. The Ailerons are used to .... the aircraft around the .... axis.

3. The Rudders are used to .... the aircraft around the .... axis.

4. Further effect of aileron is .... and of rudder is ....

5. At high airspeed the controls are .... effective and at slow airspeeds they are .... effective.

6. Slipstream from the propeller .... airflow over the .... making rudder and elevator more effective.

7. Changing power causes .... and ....

8. To relieve control forces, use the ....

9. Lowering flaps tends to cause the aircraft to .... and retracting the flaps lead to ....

10. In a descent apply .... to prevent ice forming in the intake.

Answers

No. 4

1. Pitch, Lateral.
2. Roll, Longitudinal.
3. Yaw, Vertical
   or normal.
4. Yaw, Roll.
5. More, Less.
6. Increases, Tail.
7. Pitch, Yaw.
8. Trimwheel.
9. Pitch, Sink.
10. Carburettor Heat.

Chapter 5

Taxying

5. **LESSON AIM**

   To learn how to taxy the aeroplane safely and correctly.

   ### LESSON OBJECTIVE

   By the end of the lesson you will be able to demonstrate and state the correct and safe procedures when taxying an aeroplane under a variety of conditions.

   ### AIRMANSHIP

   Handing and taking over control. Lookout. Rules for taxying. Airfield procedures and layout. Marshalling signals. Large aeroplanes; helicopters.

Basic Control Technique

Controlling the aircraft on the ground involves safe handling whilst taxying at slow speeds. The aircraft requires control in direction and rate of movement, control being achieved through the use of rudder pedals, engine thrust and brakes, independently or in combination.

Pre-taxy Checks

Before taxying is commenced the pre-taxy checks will be completed in accordance with the checklist and permission obtained from air traffic control. There is often very confined space for manoeuvring the aircraft around the parking area, therefore it is important to ensure that there are no obstructions before releasing the brakes. It is difficult, at first, to judge the distance required to manoeuvre the aircraft because of the length of the wings and distance of the tailplane. Power should be used cautiously to prevent damage occurring to other aircraft from the propeller slipstream.

Starting, Moving Off, Control of Speed and Stopping

More power is required to commence taxying than to keep the aircraft moving, as initially the inertia of the aeroplane needs to be overcome. Once the aircraft is moving, the power will need to be reduced, as otherwise the aircraft will continue accelerating. On a hard taxiway surface, a fast walking pace is the correct speed. In confined spaces or on rough ground the speed should be less. It may be necessary to use more power on a grass surface or if taxying uphill. Also more power may be needed to turn the aircraft, especially at slow speeds. Judge the speed by looking out ahead and to the side of the aircraft.

To slow the aeroplane down, reduce the power and then apply the brakes. Try not to use the brakes and power together. The technique is incorrect as it is wasteful on power and can cause wear or overheating of the brakes. When taxying it is generally advisable to keep the rpm at approximately 1000 or 1200 rpm to prevent plug fouling, so it can be necessary to brake occasionally to prevent taxying at too high a speed.

As the brakes are normally situated on the top of the rudder pedals, you should taxy with your heels on the floor to avoid inadvertent brake application. Use the brakes gently except in an emergency. You should test the brakes as soon as possible after moving out from the parking area. If the taxying area is obscured by the nose of the aircraft then turning left and right whilst taxying will enable you to clear the area ahead.

Control of Direction and Turning

Nosewheel aircraft usually have steerable nosewheel operated through the rudder pedals. Generally rudder and differential braking are used to control direction and turning. It is necessary to anticipate the rudder pedal movement required to enter and straighten out from turns. Additionally the strength and direction of the wind will be a factor. Be careful when using differential braking to manoeuvre in confined spaces, that you do not lock a wheel, as this can place unacceptable sideforces on the tyre leading to a hazard on takeoff or landing as the weakened tyre could burst.

It is necessary to hold the controls in a position to avoid the aircraft weathercocking or the tail lifting. When taxying into wind, the controls are more effective than taxying downwind. Into a strong headwind, hold the control column neutral or back. This holds the elevator neutral or up, holding the tail down and reducing the load on the nosewheel. Into a strong tailwind, hold the control column forward to move the elevator down, as this will prevent the wind lifting the tailplane and tipping the aircraft onto its nose. In a crosswind there will be a tendency for weathercocking into wind because of the large keel surface behind the mainwheels. Using the rudder pedals should assist but it may be necessary to use some differential braking. It will also be helpful to raise the into wind aileron if the crosswind is from ahead, by moving the control column into wind. If the crosswind is from behind, then hold the into wind aileron down by moving the aileron out of wind.

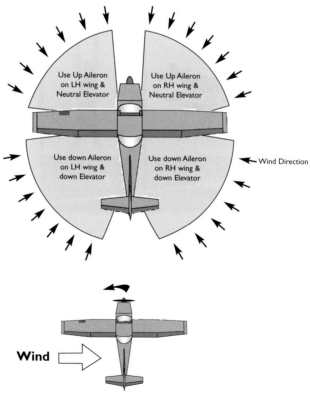

Effects of Ground Surface

Take extra care over rough or soft ground and cross ruts, ridges and joins between grass and hard surfaces at an angle of 45 degrees. Keep a careful lookout for holes and poor surface. Make sure that you taxy very slowly and carefully in the region of stones or gravel as the propeller tips may pick these up and cause damage to the propeller. There is relatively little clearance between the propeller and the ground, which is why it is important to taxy slowly to minimise the chances of hitting the propeller on the ground. If you are taxying on wet grass remember that the effectiveness of the brakes is dramatically reduced and slowing down will take longer.

Marshalling Signals

Marshaller's Position

This Bay

All Clear
(Okay)

Come
Forward

Proceed

Start
Engines

Remove
Chocks

Pilots should use similar signals for brake
& chocks with hands in front of the face.

Note: *Signals given by illuminated wands,*
bats or torches, all mean the same.

Instrument Taxy Checks

Whilst taxying you can check the functioning of certain of the flight instruments to ensure that the indications are sensible. These should only be checked once the aircraft is clear of the parking area. Turn the aircraft to the left and then to the right to check the turn coordinator and direction indicator show the turn, the balance ball shows a movement in the opposite direction and the compass and direction indicator show correct indications. The attitude indication should remain steady.

Taxying Rules (Rules of the Air)

These are part of airmanship. The pilot is Captain of the aircraft at all times even when manoeuvring on the ground. It is the pilot's responsibility to do everything possible to avoid collisions.

- Aircraft on the ground must give way to landing aircraft and those taking off and to any vehicle towing an aircraft.

- When two aircraft are taxying and approaching head-on or nearly so, each should turn right.

- Aircraft on a Converging Course - the one that has the other on his right should give way. Avoid crossing ahead of the other aircraft unless well clear.

- An aircraft being overtaken has the right of way. The overtaking aircraft must keep out of the way by turning left until well clear.

1

2

Landing aircraft has
Right of Way

Stop Give Way

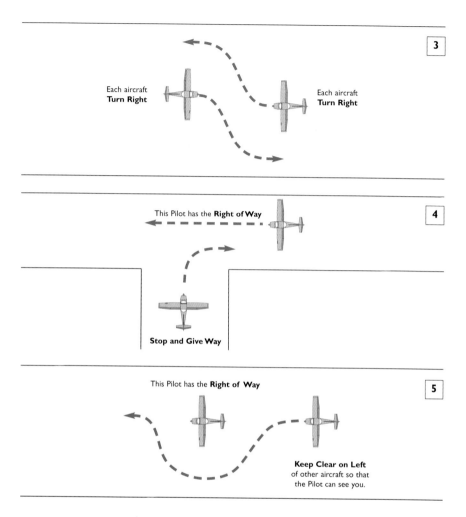

3

Each aircraft
Turn Right

Each aircraft
Turn Right

4

This Pilot has the **Right of Way**

Stop and Give Way

5

This Pilot has the **Right of Way**

Keep Clear on Left
of other aircraft so that
the Pilot can see you.

AIRMANSHIP

- Do not taxy too fast. It can lead to accidents.
- Always carry an airfield chart so that you can locate holding points and run-up areas
- Take care in the vicinity of aircraft carrying out power checks
- Listen out for air traffic messages and act on them promptly
- Be aware of other larger aeroplanes or helicopters whose jet engine efflux may blow over a light aircraft or cause damage
- If in doubt, STOP !

Left Intentionally Blank

Quiz No. 5

1. When taxying the aeroplane use a combination of .... and .... to maintain directional control.

2. Try to avoid using .... and .... together when taxying.

3. When taxying in a crosswind hold .... into wind to assist in preventing weathercocking.

4. When manoeuvring on the ground, if two aircraft are approaching head on .... should ....

Answers
No. 5

1. Brakes & Rudders.
2. Power & Brakes.
3. Ailerons.
4. Each, Turn Right.

Chapter 5 - Exercise 5E

Emergencies whilst Taxying

5E. LESSON AIM

To learn the procedures when the aircraft suffers an emergency when taxying.

LESSON OBJECTIVE

By the end of the lesson you will be able to state the correct and safe procedure when the aircraft suffers a steering or brake failure whilst taxying.

AIRMANSHIP

Taxying at the correct speed for the conditions. Other aircraft.

Steering Failure

If the steering of the nosewheel fails, then it should be possible to control the aircraft by differential braking. Stop the aircraft and then request assistance. Do not attempt to taxy it or to take off.

Brake Failure

If the brakes fail, then close the throttle and steer away from other aircraft and obstructions towards a clear area and preferably a high-friction surface such as grass.

If collision is imminent then turn off the magnetos, move the mixture control to idle cut-off and turn the fuel off. Inform air traffic then turn the Master switch off. Do not attempt to taxy the aircraft without assistance.

Left Intentionally Blank

Chapter 6

Straight and Level Flight

6.1 LESSON AIM

To learn to fly the aeroplane in a constant direction (ie. straight) and at a constant altitude (ie. level flight) and in balance.

LESSON OBJECTIVE

By the end of the lesson you will be able to maintain the aeroplane in a constant direction (straight) at a constant altitude (level) at a constant power setting and in balance.

AIRMANSHIP

Lookout (scan method). Location. Introduction to cruise checks. Work cycle.

Introduction

Straight	Level	Balance
Wings level with the horizon. Check wing tips. Establish a Reference Point. Prevent yaw with rudder. To maintain or regain Reference Point use about 5° of bank.	SELECT a sensible pitch attitude. HOLD the attitude. TRIM the elevator. CHECK altimeter for level flight. ADJUST pitch attitude if necessary.	Out-of-balance flight may be caused by **poor or false horizon.**

Out-of-balance flight may be caused by **poor or false horizon.**

A gross out-of-balance flight condition.

A slight out-of-balance flight condition.

To Maintain Level Flight
LOOKOUT.
ATTITUDE check steady.
INSTRUMENTS check altimeter/VSI.

Select - Hold - Trim

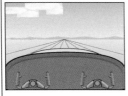

To Regain Datum Altitude
Raise or lower the nose attitude as required. When datum regained, re-select level attitude. No need to change power or trim for small errors (±100ft).

IF BALL OUT
Centre the ball with rudder and maintain straight flight with ailerons.

NOTE: **Work Cycle: LOOKOUT - ATTITUDE - INSTRUMENTS (L.A.I)**

Maintaining straight and level flight is the most fundamental exercise as it is required for good aeroplane performance and for efficient navigation amongst other things. It is also a coordination exercise bringing together all of the flying exercises you have practised so far. In order to achieve this it is helpful to consider a little theory.

Straight flight means maintaining a constant direction or heading. You will keep the aircraft wings laterally level with ailerons and coordinated use of rudder to prevent any yaw. Check that the aircraft coaming *(top of instrument panel)* is parallel with the natural horizon. Ensure that the wingtips are equidistant from the horizon. Level flight means maintaining a constant altitude which requires you to select the correct nose attitude with elevators and maintain a constant power setting. The altimeter is used to confirm you are maintaining the correct altitude. The balance ball should be central. It is also essential that the aircraft is correctly trimmed. A change in any of the variables will affect the others and therefore constant small corrections are required to maintain accurate flight.

The Forces acting on the Aeroplane

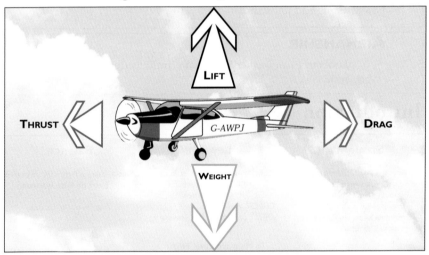

As can be seen from the diagram there are four main forces acting on the aeroplane in flight:

 LIFT which is generated by the wings

 **WEIGHT** which always acts downwards

THRUST from the propeller produced by the engine power

DRAG from the resistance to the airflow and other effects

To maintain horizontal level flight, the lift produced by the wings must equal the weight of the aircraft. The thrust should equal the drag. In this state the aircraft is in a condition of equilibrium with no tendency to accelerate. It is usual that a small balancing force is required and this will be provided by the tailplane and elevator. Normally aircraft are designed so that the tailplane provides a down force. The pilot controls this with small movements of the control column.

Couples

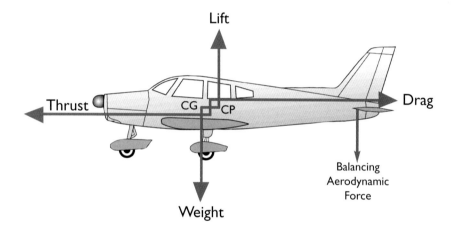

A couple is a pair of parallel opposing forces which do not act through the same point, therefore there will be a tendency to rotate. The Centre of Pressure (**CP**) is the point through which the lift acts. The weight acts through the Centre of Gravity (**CG**). If the CP is behind the CG the lift-weight couple will have a nose down effect. Normally this will be opposed by the thrust-drag couple, but if the engine stops or thrust is reduced by throttling back, the lift-weight nose down couple will allow the nose to lower which allows a safe flying speed to be maintained.

The stability of the aircraft is its ability to return to the original attitude after a disturbance. Training aeroplanes are designed to be inherently stable and thus require little pilot input to return to the original attitude.

Longitudinal Stability

This has already been considered above in the normal arrangement of lift-drag couple. If the centre of gravity (**CG**) was arranged behind the lift (**CP**), then the aeroplane would be unstable. The nose would have a tendency to rise leading to a lower airspeed.

The position of the CG is very important to the control of the aircraft in pitch. If the CG is forward, there will be a greater restoring moment from the tailplane because of greater leverage. However, if the CG is too far forward, the aircraft will become too stable and require too much control force from the elevator which will become very tiring. Additionally the elevator will become less effective at low airspeed making it difficult to flare the aircraft properly to land it. On the other hand, if the CG is too far aft, the aircraft will be less stable and being tail heavy it may stall more easily or be impossible to recover, as the elevator will no longer be effective.

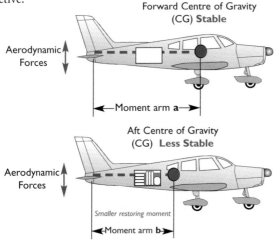

Forward Centre of Gravity (CG) **Stable**

Aerodynamic Forces

←—Moment arm **a**—→

Aft Centre of Gravity (CG) **Less Stable**

Aerodynamic Forces

Smaller restoring moment

←Moment arm **b**→

Lateral & Directional Stability

Movement of the aircraft about the longitudinal and normal axes is inter-related. You have already seen in exercise 4 that yaw produces roll and roll produces yaw. Disturbance of the aircraft from a straight path *(yaw)* presents the fin to the airflow at a greater angle of attack and this generates a restoring moment.

Lateral stability involves the rolling moments produced by sideslip. The high keel surfaces of the fin and fuselage provide the restoring moment.

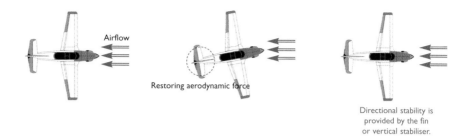

Airflow

Restoring aerodynamic force

Directional stability is
provided by the fin
or vertical stabiliser.

Some aircraft are designed to incorporate dihedral *(see below)* where the extra lift generated by the lower wing in the sideslip restores the wings to the level attitude. High wing aircraft achieve this by pendulous stability.

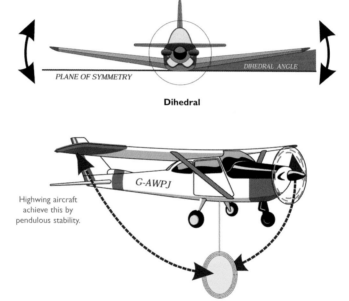

PLANE OF SYMMETRY

DIHEDRAL ANGLE

Dihedral

Highwing aircraft
achieve this by
pendulous stability.

G-AWPJ

Pendulous Stability

Since the stability of the aircraft is not as great in the rolling and yawing planes as in the pitching plane, a disturbance in either roll or yaw leads to a spiral descent if unchecked by the pilot. Normally the aircraft's natural stability assists the maintenance of straight and level flight and it should be possible to achieve trimmed hands off flight.

Lift

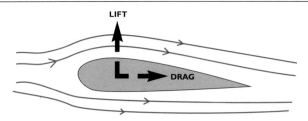

The aerofoil shape of the wings is such that the airflow speeds up over the upper surface which reduces the static pressure and creates an upward aerodynamic force. The vertical component is lift and the component parallel to the flight path is called induced drag – it is a by-product of lift.

The ability of a wing to lift is called the coefficient of lift and it depends on the shape of the wing and its angle of attack. The angle of attack is the angle between the relative airflow and the chord line of the aerofoil. This is not the same as the pitch attitude which is measured relative to the horizon.

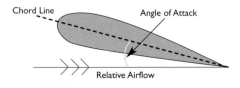

Inertia

The aircraft is resistant to change of direction or flightpath because of its inertia and thus it will continue on its original flight path briefly before adopting the newly selected attitude. Thus it is essential to wait for a moment before trimming or otherwise adjusting the aircraft in order to enable the input to take effect.

Power Setting

There will be a particular power setting for your aircraft which, when combined with the correct attitude, will maintain straight and level flight. The often used phrase is:

Power plus Attitude = Performance

If the nose is too high the aircraft will climb and vice versa. You can use the altimeter and VS1 to check if the aircraft is deviating from the correct attitude.

Small movements of the control wheel can be used to correct changes before they develop. Reselect the correct attitude, hold it, pause and then retrim if necessary.

Keeping the aircraft in trim will make flying accurately more comfortable. Always select the attitude first before trimming. It is possible to fly with the controls crossed i.e. one wing a little lower than the other and the aeroplane out of balance. This might occur accidentally if the horizon is indistinct, as you may line up the aircraft with a line of hills or sloping cloudbank. The problem is that this is an uncomfortable way to fly the aeroplane and also inefficient as performance is reduced because of the increase in drag. To prevent this, make sure that the balance ball is kept in the middle and use a ground feature to maintain your constant direction with ailerons.

Lookout

As your training continues, you will gradually take on more responsibility for the lookout. Airmanship is of prime importance and the lookout is key to good airmanship. Because the eye tends to focus only about a metre in front of your face if there is no focal target, it is necessary to move the eyes in a regular scan pattern to ensure that you notice any conflicting traffic in good time. The sky should be divided up into segments. A series of movements should be made up and down only pausing for a moment before continuing. Your eyes should be looking outside the cockpit for most of the time. If you need to refer to an instrument such as the altimeter, then only glance at it briefly in order to absorb the required data before reverting to your scan. Be aware of your blind spot about 30° from your forward gaze and often blocked by the framework around the windshield. Move your head to reduce this problem.

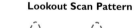

Lookout Scan Pattern

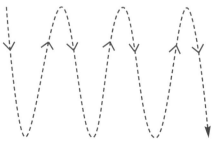

Cruise Checks

Straight and level flight is also termed "**the cruise**". As part of good airmanship your instructor will gradually introduce you to regular cruise checks, including monitoring the fuel state and rate of consumption, checking the engine temperature and pressure, alternator and suction readings, resynchronising the direction indicator with the magnetic compass and ensuring the carburettor heat is applied regularly to prevent ice formation. You will learn a mnemonic such as "**FREDA**" to help you to remember the checks.

F	**Fuel** - Check quantities, change tanks if necessary	
R	**Radios** - Check on correct frequency	
E	**Engine** - Check for Carburettor Ice, Monitor Temperatures & Pressures.	
D	**Direction** - Check Direction Indicator synchronised with Compass.	
A	**Altimeter** - Check Correct Pressure Setting is indicated.	

Quiz No. 6.1

1. Lift on the aircraft must be equalled by the ....

2. Thrust equals ....

3. If the centre of gravity is forward, the .... provides a greater .... moment to maintain longitudinal stability.

4. Lateral stability is achieved through the restoring moments of the .... and ....

5. Power + ... = Performance

6. Lookout is achieved by using the .... technique and you identify aircraft to your instructor using the ....

Answers
No. 6.1

1.   Weight.
2.   Drag.
3.   Tail, Restoring.
4.   Fin & Fuselage.
5.   Attitude.
6.   Scan, Clock Code.

Chapter 6 - *Exercise 6 (Part 2)*

Straight and Level Flight at different Airspeeds

Exercise 6	Straight & Level Part 2 of 3

LESSON AIM
To Fly Straight and Level whilst changing Power and/or Airspeed.

AIRMANSHIP
Lookout (Scan Method). Location. Introduction to CRUISE checks.
WORK CYCLE L.A.I.

AIR EXERCISE   *To Revise Straight and Level Flight.*

Teaching Points

Straight & Level at various Power Settings

At a **higher power setting** a lower nose attitude will be required to maintain a constant altitude (note high speed).
At a **lower power setting** a higher nose attitude is required to maintain a constant altitude (note lower airspeed).

Straight & Level at Selected Airspeeds

High to Low Airspeed
Reduce power to less than required, progressively raise nose to maintain altitude.
Increase power to that required when approaching desired airspeed, then trim.

Low to High Airspeed
Increase power to more than required, progressively lower nose to maintain altitude.
Decrease power to that required when approaching desired airspeed, then trim.

Note: Prevent Yaw with rudder while increasing/decreasing Power and Speed.

L-A-I   LOOKOUT - ATTITUDE - INSTRUMENTS

An aircraft can maintain level flight at a range of different airspeeds from a high-speed cruise to very low speed just above the stall as is used for landing.

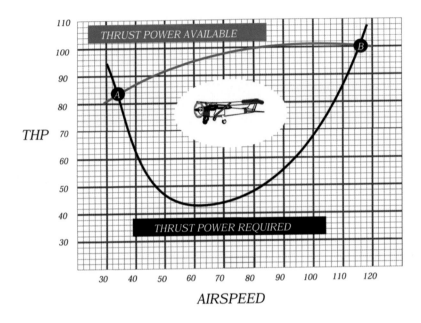

THP

AIRSPEED

Ⓐ The **minimum speed** at which the aircraft can be flown in level flight.
Ⓑ The **maximum speed** at which the aircraft can be flown in level flight.

Power + Attitude = **Performance**

From the above graph it can be seen that it is possible to fly the aircraft at two different airspeeds for the same power setting.

You can see that the amount of drag increases markedly at the lower speed end of the power curve.

Changing Airspeed

Every time you wish to accelerate or decelerate the aircraft you will also have to change the attitude because otherwise the aircraft will not maintain level flight. The thrust has to balance the drag. When selecting a specific airspeed at which to fly it is necessary to make a power change then allow the aircraft to accelerate or decelerate until it approaches the target airspeed and then adjust the power setting to maintain level flight. Of course a change in power and attitude will require a change of trim.

Remember that when you make a power change there will also be pitch and yaw. These need to be anticipated and prevented in order to maintain smooth and controlled flight.

Best Endurance Speed

This is the speed to fly for maximum time airborne for the least fuel consumption. You should fly at the minimum power airspeed. This is useful if you have to hold for some reason to await landing at an airport or to await an improvement in the weather.

Best Range Speed

This is the speed to fly to cover the greatest distance on the available fuel. The airspeed will be the speed at which the lift/drag ratio is best. See the graph below. These speeds are set out in the Pilot's Operating Handbook for your aircraft and are calculated on the basis that the correct leaning of the mixture technique has been used.

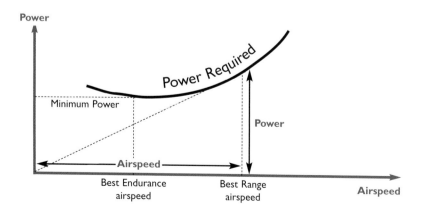

Left Intentionally Blank

Chapter 6 - Exercise 6 (Part 3)

Straight & Level Flight at different Flap Settings

LESSON AIM
To Fly the Aircraft at a slow safe cruise with improved forward visibility.

AIRMANSHIP
As on previous exercise. *Note:* Flap Limitations, Operational Technique & Flap Indications. **(L-O-I)**.

AIR EXERCISE   *To Revise Straight and Level Flight.*

Teaching Points

Straight & Level at various Flap Settings

Entry:
1) Select Power.
2) Establish the aeroplane in straight and level flight in a "**clean configuration**".

To Lower the Flap:
1) Ensure airspeed is below maximum flap extension speed *(V_{FE})(Limitation)*.
2) Extend flaps in stages *(Operation and Indication)*.
3) Progressively select lower nose attitude *(this avoids ballooning & maintains altitude)*.
4) Adjust power to maintain desired airspeed.
5) Trim out elevator pressure for each stage of flap.

To Raise the Flap:
1) Check that the airspeed is at a safe margin above the stall.
2) Raise the flaps in stages, holding the nose in a higher attitude to prevent "**sink**" and maintain altitude.
3) Check flap indication.

You may wish to fly straight and level with flap extended in order to fly more slowly but with better forward visibility in order to inspect a field for a precautionary landing or to give yourself more time to locate your position.

Lowering flaps will increase the drag and therefore greater power will be required to maintain the airspeed. There will also be an increase in lift produced by the changed shape of the aerofoil; thus a lower nose attitude will be required to prevent the aircraft gaining altitude. You will need to anticipate the effect of ballooning as the flap is lowered in order to remain level.

Be careful not to lower flap when the airspeed is above V_{FE} as this can lead to structural damage.

When raising flap anticipate the sinking and make a small power change to maintain airspeed. Do not raise the flaps if the airspeed is below the "**clean**" stalling speed. Trim the aircraft to remove any residual control pressures.

Chapter 7 - *Exercise 7 (Part 1)*

Climbing

LESSON AIM

To Learn to Enter and Maintain a Climb on a constant Heading and in Balance and at the correct Climb Speed.

LESSON OBJECTIVE

By the end of the lesson you will be able to demonstrate safely and correctly your ability to fly the aeroplane and maintain a climb on a constant heading and in balance.

AIRMANSHIP

Lookout. Engine Considerations. Blind Spot. Cloud. Airspace.

AIR EXERCISE   *Climbing.*

Teaching Points

Entry:

1) Lookout, check temperature and pressures.
2) Mixture rich.
3) **P** - Apply full power (prevent yaw).
4) **A** - Select pitch attitude. Hold.
5) Wait for airspeed to settle.
6) **T** - Trim. Check airspeed.
7) Adjust attitude if required.

During Climb:

1) Lookout.
2) Blind spot.
3) Check temperature and pressures.
4) Check direction, airspeed and balance.

Note: Elevator Controls Attitude and Airspeed.

Levelling Off:

1) **A**nticipate, then at approximately 10% of the rate of climb, select a level attitude.
2) As airspeed increases, progressively lower the nose attitude to maintain altitude.
3) Reduce **P**ower, prevent yaw, **T**rim.

95

┌───┐
│ **LESSON OBJECTIVE**   │
│   By the end of the lesson you will be able to demonstrate safely │
│   and correctly your ability to fly the aeroplane and maintain a climb on a │
│   constant heading and in balance.   │
└───┘

┌───┐
│ **AIRMANSHIP**   │
│   Lookout. Engine Considerations. Blind Spot. Cloud. Airspace. │
└───┘

Introduction

Forces in the Climb

For a steady climb, the thrust must equal the drag and the excess thrust will also provide a small vertical component of lift. See diagram below

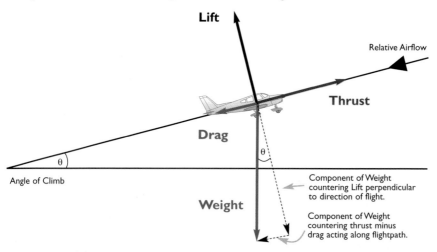

It can be seen that there is also a component of weight acting backwards along the flight path and this is additional to the drag. The balance of forces to achieve equilibrium is more complicated than in level flight. Surprisingly, the wing lift is less in climbing flight than in level flight, as a component of thrust opposes a component of weight.

Power/Airspeed and Rate of Climb

In a training aeroplane the power required to climb the aircraft is usually the maximum available i.e. full power.

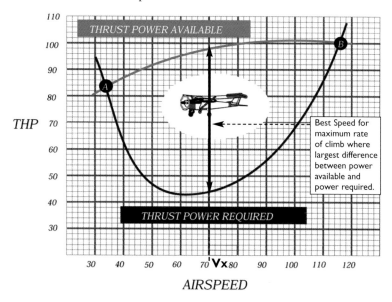

> **Ⓐ** The **minimum speed** at which the aircraft can be flown in level flight.
> **Ⓑ** The **maximum speed** at which the aircraft can be flown in level flight.
>
> ## Power + Attitude = **Performance**

From the graph it can be seen that the rate of climb will be less when the power required is close to the power available and will be highest where the curves are widest apart. The Pilot's Operating Handbook will contain the speeds for best rate of climb, cruise climb and best angle of climb.

Engine Considerations

During the climb, the engine is operating very close to or at full power. It is necessary to monitor the temperature and pressure gauges frequently to ensure that there is no overheating. The problem of possible overheating is exacerbated by the reduced cooling airflow due to the lower airspeed. Additionally during the climb, it is usual to ensure that the mixture is set to full rich, as the effect of greater fuel through the engine assists with cooling the cylinders.

Setting up the Climb

Airmanship as always is a prime consideration. A thorough lookout must be carried out particularly above and ahead of the aircraft and consideration must be given to the presence of cloud or controlled airspace. It is useful to select a reference point to the side of the nose of the aircraft before commencing the climb as the higher nose attitude in the manoeuvre will reduce the ability of the pilot to use the horizon for reference.

The Entry to the Climb

Apply full power and counteract the tendency to yaw with rudder. The aircraft nose should be raised to the approximate climbing attitude and held steady whilst the airspeed settles. Check the wingtips to ensure there is no bank present. Then the nose attitude should be adjusted to achieve the required climbing speed. Trim the aircraft so the attitude remains steady.

PAT : POWER - ATTITUDE - TRIM

Maintaining the Climb

Use the ailerons, rudder and elevator to maintain the climb attitude. Since you have a very high nose attitude in the climb, your view ahead is restricted so in the interests of good airmanship, you should weave the nose from side to side every 500 feet to clear the area ahead and beneath the nose. Check the temperatures and pressures and if the engine starts to overheat then lower the nose slightly to improve the flow of cooling air.

Levelling Off

As you approach the required altitude anticipate levelling off by about 10% of the rate of climb. Start gradually lowering the nose to select the straight and level attitude. Allow the aeroplane to accelerate and as the cruise speed is reached select the cruise power setting. Hold the attitude and trim the aircraft so the attitude remains steady.

APT : ATTITUDE - POWER - TRIM

Once level consider leaning the mixture, check the carburettor heat and continue monitoring engine temperatures and pressures.

Quiz No. 7

1. There is less lift in a climb than straight and level flight because a .... of .... opposes a .... of ....

2. During a Climb you need to monitor the .... and .... frequently to prevent overheating.

3. To enter the Climb, apply full power and use .... to counteract ....

4. When levelling off from the climb select .... first and only when .... is achieved, reduce.........

Answers

No. 7

1.   Component, Thrust, Component, Weight.
2.   Temperatures, Pressures.
3.   Rudder, the tendency to Yaw.
4.   Attitude, Cruise Speed, Power.

Chapter 7 - *Exercise 7 (Part 2)*

Climbing with Flaps, V_X and V_Y Climbs

CLIMBING WITH FLAP

1) Reduces the take-off run.
2) Allows the same lift to be generated at a lower airspeed.
3) Reduces the stalling speed.
4) May enable a steeper climb-out angle to be achieved (depending on the type of aeroplane).

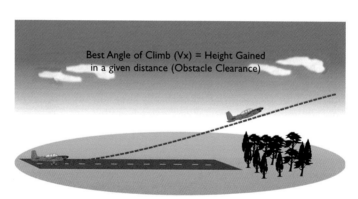

Best Angle of Climb (Vx) = Height Gained in a given distance (Obstacle Clearance)

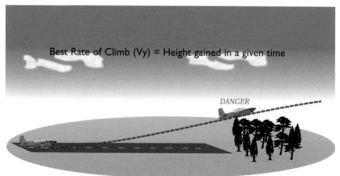

Best Rate of Climb (Vy) = Height gained in a given time

DANGER

Climbing with Flaps

Sometimes it is desirable to take off with some flap extended, particularly on a short runway as more lift can be generated at a slower airspeed, which will shorten the takeoff run and reduce the stalling speed. It may also permit a steeper climb-out angle to be achieved improving obstacle clearance. The effect of climbing with flap will be to reduce the rate of climb slightly, but with full flap this would reduce drastically because of the increase in drag. Therefore it is usual only to use the first stage of flap in the climb. Take care when retracting the flap as the aircraft will tend to sink. Wait until a safe altitude of at least 200 feet a.g.l. has been reached. Adjust the attitude to maintain the climb speed and then trim.

Vx Climbs

Maximum angle of climb is required to clear obstacles and gain the greatest height in the minimum distance travelled. The maximum angle of climb speed occurs where the greatest difference between the thrust which is available during the climb and the thrust which is required. Excess thrust is that which is available over and above the drag. *(Power can be defined as the result of thrust x velocity, so for a fixed power output, the greater the velocity, the lower the thrust).* During the maximum angle of climb the lower airspeed means even less engine cooling but normally this type of climb is only used for a short period immediately after take off so there should be no need for any additional considerations on engine handling.

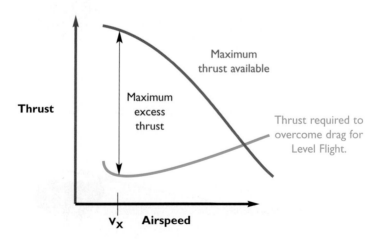

V_Y Climbs

Maximum rate of climb speed exists where there is the greatest difference between power required and power available, ie. maximum excess power. *See diagram on page 97.*

Cruise Climbs

The objective is to obtain a reasonable rate of climb as well as a higher speed across the ground than in a normal climb. Better forward visibility will improve the lookout and better engine cooling will be achieved by the increased airflow through the intakes.

Left Intentionally Blank

Chapter 8, Part 1

Descending

8. LESSON AIM	To learn the procedures and controls to place the aeroplane into a glide descent at best glide speed and to maintain the glide.

AIRMANSHIP

Lookout. Engine considerations. Airspace. Altimeter settings and ground clearance.

The Glide

The Forces in the Glide

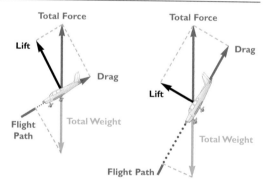

1. By lowering the nose into a steady glide a component of weight acts as thrust.

2. The sum of lift and drag oppose weight.

When the thrust is removed, the aircraft will tend to pitch nose down and a component of the weight will act along the flightpath to balance the drag. As you can see from the diagram, the remaining forces, lift and drag will oppose the weight and a steady glide will be achieved when the three forces are in equilibrium. The steeper the glide angle, the faster the glide speed. Also, using flaps will steepen the glide angle if you are trying to maintain the same speed as the drag will increase on lowering flap.

Gliding Range

The range an aircraft can travel in a glide will depend on its Lift/Drag ratio.

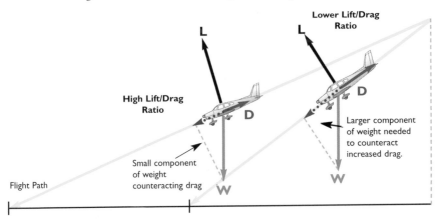

If you are in a glide because your engine has failed, you would want to travel as far as possible over the ground with minimum height loss. Therefore you would want a very shallow glide angle *(see diag above)*. If you select the wrong airspeed i.e. angle of attack then your gliding range will be reduced, so you must check the Pilots Operating Handbook to find the best glide speed for your aircraft.

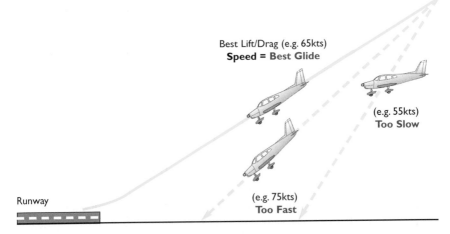

If your aircraft has a Lift/Drag ratio of say, 9:1 it will glide approximately 9000 feet for a height loss of 1000 feet, which is around 1.5 nm. You will only achieve this performance at the correct glide speed.

Effect of Wind

The effect of a headwind or tailwind on your glide can be seen by examining the diag below:

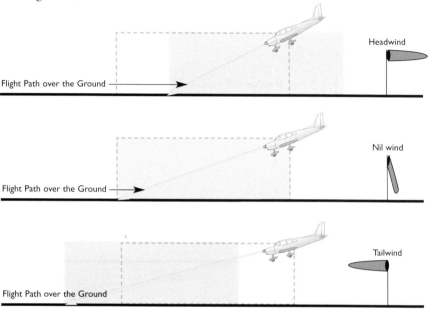

Thus with a tailwind the glide range will be increased and into a headwind it will be reduced. Into a headwind you could increase the speed slightly to cover more ground. Generally though it is preferable to maintain a constant airspeed and the technique is not often taught, because of many variable factors.

Effect of Weight

If you fly the aircraft at the correct angle of attack then weight will not affect gliding range. However, the best glide speed will be increased by approximately 5% for a weight increase of 10%. Clearly since there is no angle of attack indicator in light training aircraft it would appear that you would need to know a range of possible glide speeds according to the weight of the aircraft. In practice the difference is fairly small and therefore the speed set out in the **POH** will usually be sufficiently accurate for most configurations. The best gliding speed is normally quoted at maximum all up weight.

Glide for Endurance

If you wish to remain airborne for as long as possible rather than maximising distance covered in the glide *(e.g. because you want to try to restart the engine)* you need to use an airspeed to achieve minimum descent. This speed will be less than the best glide speed and equivalent to that used for minimum power required.

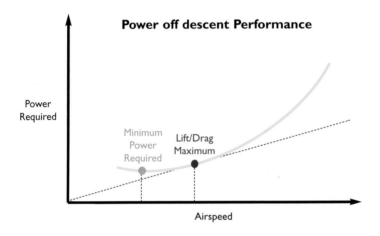

Exercise 8   Descending Part 1 of 3

LESSON AIM

To Learn the Procedures and Controls to place the aeroplane into a Gliding Descent at Best Glide Speed and Maintain the Glide.

AIRMANSHIP

Lookout. Engine Considerations. Airspace. Altimeter Settings and Ground Clearance.

AIR EXERCISE   *Descending.*

Teaching Points

Entry:

1) Lookout, check temperature, pressure, enrichen mixture.
2) Carburettor heat on.
3) **P** - Close throttle (prevent yaw). Hold attitude. Then ..
4) **A** - Select required glide attitude.
5) **T** - Trim.
6) Check ASI.
7) Adjust attitude if required.
8) Re-trim if required.

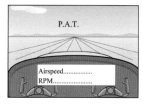

During Descent:

1) Lookout.
2) Blind spot. Weave nose.
3) Check temperature and pressures.
4) Warm engine.
5) Note rate of descent.

Note: Elevator Controls Attitude and Airspeed.

Levelling Off:

1) Carburettor heat off.
2) Anticipate by approximately 10% of the rate of descent.
3) Increase **P**ower to cruise, prevent yaw.
4) Select level **A**ttitude. **T**rim.
5) Check ASI.
6) Adjust power and/or attitude if required.

Work Cycle L.A.I

Prior to commencing the glide, ensure that you have carried out a good lookout, including clearing the blind spot under the nose. Having checked that the mixture is set to rich, apply carburettor heat to full hot prior to closing the throttle. *(See carb heat supplement for reasons.)* Anticipate the pitch down as you close the throttle and prevent yaw.

Initially hold the level attitude and as the aircraft decelerates towards the glide speed, lower the nose attitude slightly to maintain the chosen glide speed. Trim the pressures off *(there may be a large amount of backwards trimming required)*. Allow the speed to settle and adjust as necessary, retrimming as required.

Once settled in the glide maintain the airspeed and every 500 feet clear the blind spot by weaving the nose. Additionally warm the engine by opening the throttle to a count of three and then closing it again. This will ensure that warm oil continues to circulate around the engine and that there is not uneven cooling in the cylinders. The work cycle should be:

LAI : Lookout - Attitude - Instruments

Levelling Off or Entering the Climb

When you want to level off from the glide it will be necessary to anticipate by about 10% of the rate of descent. Start to select the straight and level attitude as you smoothly apply cruise power. *(Do not forget to return the carb heat to cold.)* Be aware that the pitching and yawing moments from the glide to level cruise may be very strong and you will need to counteract these positively. Coarse trim the control force and then as the aircraft accelerates to cruise speed, fine tune and retrim to achieve hands off straight and level flight.

If you wish instead to enter a climb from a glide *(this might be the case if you are practising glide approaches in the circuit and elect to go around from a poorly judged glide)*, the same procedure will apply, except that full power will be required. The pitch up and yaw will be even more pronounced, but you can harness the pitching moment to assist in selecting the climbing attitude.

Power - Attitude - Trim

Quiz No. 8

1. The distance an aircraft can travel in a glide depends on its ..../.......... ratio.

2. Wind affects the glide by .... distance with a tailwind and .... distance with a headwind.

3. Increasing weight affects glidespeed by an .... of .... % for an increased weight of .... %

4. It is good airmanship to .... every 500 feet in the glide.

Answers
No. 8

1. Lift / Drag.
2. Increasing,
   Decreasing
3. Increase of 5, 10
4. Warm the Engine.

Chapter 8 - Exercise 8 (Part 2)

Descending

The Cruise or Powered Descent

The addition of power will reduce the rate of descent, as the thrust will balance some of the drag. There will be less need for the component of weight acting along the flightpath, hence the pitch attitude can be less steep. Thus adding power will flatten the descent ie reduce the rate of descent and reducing power will steepen the descent and increase the rate of descent. A cruise descent will be achieved by reducing power slightly and maintaining a cruise airspeed. This has the benefit of maintaining a constant speed which is helpful in navigation planning and also eliminating shock cooling of the engine which might occur if the descent was carried out as a glide.

Power Controls RATE OF DESCENT

Descending with Flap

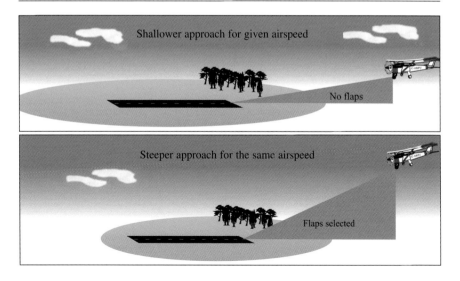

Use of flap in the descent will cause a small increase in lift and a significant increase in drag as the shape of the wing alters. Remember not to lower flap if the airspeed is greater than the maximum flap extension speed (V_{FE}). To maintain a constant airspeed you will need to counteract the natural pitching tendency and then lower the nose with elevator a further amount each time another stage of flap is selected. You will notice an increased rate of descent with each stage of flap selected. The benefit of this is that you have a steeper approach path without increasing the airspeed and your forward visibility is greatly improved on the approach to land.

Elevator Controls Airspeed (i.e. Pitch Attitude)

Retracting flap will lead to a sink if not anticipated with back pressure. Make sure the airspeed is not too low *(i.e. below the green arc on the ASI)* as the stall speed with flaps extended is lower than the "**clean**" stall speed. Retract flaps in stages trimming between each stage.

Approach and Go-around

Normally flaps will be used on the approach and not raised during this time as the intention will be to land. However if a missed approach or "**go around**" has to be executed the high drag from landing flap will degrade the ability of the aircraft to climb out. Therefore it will be necessary to retract the "**drag**" flap or "**landing flap**" once full power has been applied and the aircraft is established at a safe speed in the level or a shallow climbing attitude. *(see Chapter 13 for more detail of this manoeuvre)*.

See overleaf page 21a from Pre-Flight Briefing.

LESSON AIM

To Learn how to Control the Descent by the use of POWER and/or FLAPS.

AIRMANSHIP

Lookout (esp. Below), Location, Ref Pt, Engine Management (C/H, T & P's), V_{FE}, V_{S1}.

AIR EXERCISE   *Practise Exercise 8 Part 1.*

Teaching Points

Effect of Flap

1) Enter a **GLIDE** best glide speed.
Note: **ROD**
2) Check V_{FE} 10° Flap.
3) Pitch **DOWN** for best glide speed.
4) **TRIM**.
Note: **ROD** increases.
5) 20° Flap.
6) Pitch **DOWN** for best glide speed.
7) **TRIM**.
Note: **ROD** increases.
5) 30° Flap.
6) Pitch **DOWN** for best glide speed.
7) **TRIM**.
Note: **ROD** increases even further.
8) Retract flaps in stages.
9) Pitch **UP** for best glide speed.
10) **TRIM** between each stage.
Note: **ROD** decreases for each stage.

Effect of Power

1) Enter a **GLIDE** best glide speed.
Note: **ROD**
2) Increase Power to approx. 1600 RPM.
3) Raise Pitch Attitude to maintain
   say 65 kts.
4) **TRIM** (Select - Hold - Trim).
Note: **ROD** reduces.
5) Increase Power by 200 RPM.
6) Raise Pitch Attitude to maintain 65kts.
7) **TRIM**.
Note: **ROD** reduces.
8) Reduce Power at 200 RPM intervals.
9) Lower Pitch Attitudes to maintain 65kts
10) **TRIM** between each stage.
Note: **ROD** increases

Effect of Power & Flap

Normal Approach Configuration
S & L (Intermediate Speed).
1) Reduce Power (C/H On).
2) Back Px to maintain Alt & prevent Yaw.
3) Check V_{FE} 20° Flap.
4) Pitch **DOWN** for approach speed.
5) **TRIM** (very small amount).
Note: **ROD**

Final Approach Configuration
6) 30° Flap
7) Maintain **ATTITUDE** for final approach speed.
8) **TRIM**.

Missed Approach

"Go Around !!"
1) C/H Off.
2) **FULL** Power.
3) Prevent **YAW**.
4) Pitch **UP** to Horizon.
5) Retract **DRAG** Flap.
6) Adjust Climb Attitude.
7) **POSITIVE ROC.**
8) Retract Flap in Stages & adjust Climb Attitude.
9) **TRIM** for V_Y or V_X.
Note: Very Strong CC Forces Possible.

Elevator Controls Airspeed • Power Controls ROD • Pitch Attitude Controls Airspeed

Work Cycle: LOOKOUT - ATTITUDE - INSTRUMENTS

Note: Flap Settings, Power Settings & Speeds are representative for a Cessna 152.

Sideslip or Emergency Descent

A sideslip is a manoeuvre used to increase the rate of descent particularly if no flaps are fitted. It is an unnatural manoeuvre which will feel a little uncomfortable as the aircraft will be out of balance.

To enter a sideslip the aircraft will be banked with aileron, but opposite rudder will be applied to maintain a straight flight path, thus the controls are said to be "crossed". This will create a lot of extra drag which will increase the rate of descent. You will also need to maintain forward pressure on the control column to maintain the airspeed.

Problems

It is likely that the POH will restrict the use of a sideslip when flaps are extended as the effect of lowering flap will have blanked off part of the rudder and elevator thereby reducing their effectiveness. Another problem which will become apparent in some aircraft is that the position of the pitot and static vents may lead to erroneous readings on the ASI due to the sideways movement of the aircraft compared with the relative airflow.

V_{NE} Dive

This is an emergency procedure which might be adopted if there was a fire in the engine. Diving the aircraft at high speed might assist in extinguishing the fire. The aircraft would be dived at the maximum structural speed and care must be taken not to overstress the aircraft controls in such a configuration, thus only limited control movements and manoeuvring are permitted. If the air is turbulent then the manoeuvre must be limited to the maximum rough airspeed (V_A).

AIRMANSHIP

In addition to the points of airmanship covered above, it is important to remain aware of the location of the aircraft when you are descending. Ensure that you have the correct altimeter setting and that you do not inadvertently breach any of the low flying rules set out in rule 5 of the Rules of the Air *(see Volume 2 for more details)*. Maintain a good lookout at all times, remembering to clear the blind spot regularly. Keep monitoring the engine temperatures and pressures and apply carb heat regularly *(keeping it set to full hot if you are in a glide or have a low power setting selected for the descent rate required)*.

Chapter 9

Turning - The Medium Level Turn

9. Lesson Aim

To learn to enter and maintain a medium level banked turn (30°)

Lesson Objective

By the end of the lesson you will be able to demonstrate safely and correctly your ability to enter a medium level banked turn and to roll out on a selected reference feature and later onto selected headings.

Airmanship

Lookout. Blind spot. Cloud. Orientation. Airspace.

Forces in the Turn

In order to turn the aircraft a sideways force is required and in normal flight this is provided by banking the aircraft and tilting the lift force. The result is two components of lift acting at right angles to each other. The horizontal component which is acting in the direction of the turn is called centripetal force. Centrifugal force acts to oppose the centripetal force. The aircraft is no longer in equilibrium. The lift force has been tilted and its vertical component reduced thus either altitude will be lost or the airspeed will reduce if the pilot tries to increase the angle of attack to maintain the altitude.

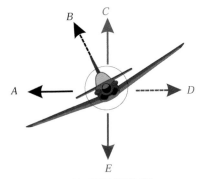

A HORIZONTAL COMPONENT.
B TOTAL LIFT.
C VERTICAL COMPONENT.
D CENTRIFUGAL FORCE.
E WEIGHT.

LOAD FACTOR IS THE RATIO BETWEEN LIFT & WEIGHT & IS DETERMINED BY -

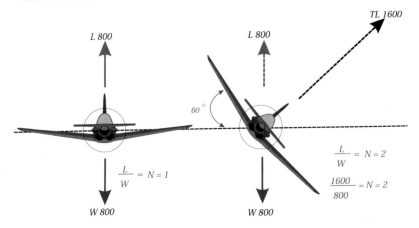

$$\frac{L}{W} = N = 1$$

$$\frac{L}{W} = N = 2$$

$$\frac{1600}{800} = N = 2$$

It can be seen from the above diagram that the stall speed will increase in the turn because of the increased load factor. The wings will also be at a higher angle of attack and therefore producing more drag as a result of the increased lift required to sustain the greater load.

The performance of the aircraft in a steady turn can be measured by rate of turn and turning radius. When an aircraft is in a correctly balanced turn at a constant angle of bank and constant airspeed the rate of turn and turn radius are fixed irrespective of weight. The rate of turn at a given airspeed will depend on the amount of horizontal lift component and this will be directly in proportion to the amount of bank. The rate of turn at a given airspeed increases as the angle of bank increases. The radius of turn will be least for a given angle of bank at the lowest airspeed.

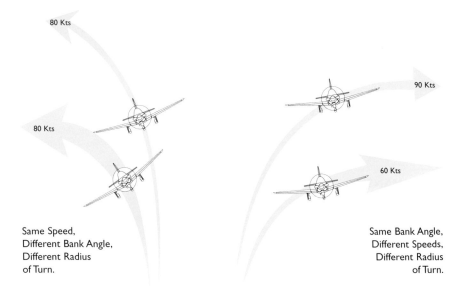

80 Kts

90 Kts

80 Kts

60 Kts

Same Speed,
Different Bank Angle,
Different Radius
of Turn.

Same Bank Angle,
Different Speeds,
Different Radius
of Turn.

A medium level turn is a balanced turn performed at a moderate bank angle, usually 30 degrees. Constant power is used and the aircraft should maintain altitude throughout. You will also practise rate one turns *(see later)*, climbing and descending turns and steep turns *(see Chapter 15)* of 45 degrees of bank or more.

LESSON AIM

To Learn to Enter and Maintain a Medium Level Banked Turn (30°)

LESSON OBJECTIVE

By the end of the lesson you will be able to demonstrate safely and correctly your ability to enter a medium level banked turn and roll-out on a selected reference feature and later onto selected headings.

AIRMANSHIP

Lookout. Blind Spot. Cloud. Orientation. Airspace.

AIR EXERCISE   *Medium turns at 30° of bank.*

Teaching Points

Entry

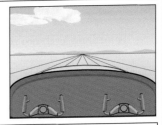

1) Use Reference Point.
2) Lookout.
3) Aileron to roll into 30° bank.
4) Rudder in the direction of the turn to prevent unwanted yaw and to maintain balance.
5) Back pressure on elevators to maintain altitude.
6) Centralise ailerons.

In the Turn

1) Lookout.
2) Ailerons to maintain bank.
3) Elevator to maintain nose attitude/altitude.
4) Rudder to maintain balance.
5) Note the loss in airspeed.

Recovery

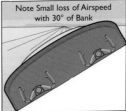

Note Small loss of Airspeed with 30° of Bank

1) Anticipation of heading or reference point.
2) Ailerons to roll the wings level.
3) Rudder to prevent unwanted yaw and to maintain balance.
4) Elevator to maintain level flight.
5) Adjust as required.
6) Lookout.

NB. Note different Nose Attitudes between turns Left and Right (caused by side-by-side seating).

Work Cycle: L - A - I

Having carried out a good lookout *(particularly in the direction of turn)* use ailerons to select the correct bank angle, centralising the control wheel to hold the angle, balance with rudder to remove any unwanted yaw and apply a little back pressure with elevator. This is a coordinated manoeuvre and should be carried out smoothly. We have already seen in exercise 4 how the effect of applying bank will also lead to a little unwanted yaw when the ailerons are being deflected. Use sufficient rudder to prevent adverse yaw especially entering and rolling out of the turn.

During the turn, the upper wing is travelling faster than the lower wing and it may be necessary to hold off bank to maintain a constant bank angle. In medium turns the slight loss of airspeed which will result from the increased bank pressure (angle of attack) is acceptable. You should note the position of the cowling relative to the horizon and maintain a continuous lookout throughout. It is a good idea to check the attitude indicator to verify the bank angle and occasionally scan the balance ball and altimeter.

Work Cycle : L A I

Initially you will be using a reference feature to roll out of the turn, but as you become more proficient, your instructor will get you to roll out onto selected headings using the direction indicator (**DI**). You need to anticipate the recovery to level flight by approximately 10 degrees, smoothly coordinating the rollout, with aileron, rudder and elevator.

The most important factor to appreciate in turns in an aircraft with side by side seating, is that the picture outside will be very different when turning left and right. It will appear as if the nose attitude is far higher when turning right when you are in the left hand seat and this can lead to a tendency to try to lower the nose on entering the right turn, leading to a loss of altitude. Conversely there can be a tendency to raise the nose when entering a turn to the left. You should not trim the aircraft in the turn as turning is a transient manoeuvre.

Rate One Turns

A rate one turn is a turn which will achieve 360° in 2 minutes thus the heading change is 3° per second. This turn is marked on the turn coordinator and is the standard angle of bank used in instrument flying. The bank angle required will be dependent on the airspeed and can be calculated as follows:

If the airspeed is marked in knots simply divide the airspeed by 10 and add 7 to obtain the bank angle required in degrees. If your ASI is indicated in mph then divide by 10 and add 5.

eg.   90 knots: $\dfrac{90}{10} + 7$ =   9 + 7 = 16° bank angle

80 mph: $\dfrac{80}{10} + 5$ =   8 + 5 = 13° bank angle

Chapter 9 - Exercise 9 (Part 2)

Climbing & Descending Turns

LESSON AIM

To Learn the Procedures and Controls to place the aeroplane into a Climbing or Descending Turn.

LESSON OBJECTIVE

By the end of the lesson you will be able to demonstrate safely and correctly your ability to place the aeroplane into different climbing and descending turning configurations.

AIRMANSHIP

Lookout. Blind Spot. Cloud. Orientation. Airspace.

AIR EXERCISE   *Medium turns, Climbing and Descending, at 15° to 30° of bank.*

Teaching Points

Climbing Turns 15° Only

1) Enter climb, select 15° bank angle. Adjust attitude to maintain climb airspeed.
2) Elevators control airspeed - rudder to maintain balance.
3) A lower nose attitude is required than that of straight climb to maintain the same airspeed.
4) Aeroplane tends to overbank.

Descending Turns Up to 30° of Bank

1) Fly as for medium turns.
2) Elevators control airspeed - rudder to prevent unwanted yaw and to maintain balance.
3) A lower nose attitude is required than that of straight descent to maintain the same airspeed.
4) Aeroplane tends to roll out of the turn.

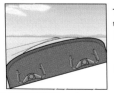

Turns to the left and to the right show an apparent difference in nose attitude in aeroplanes with side-by-side seating arrangements.

Climbing and descending turns will also be practised with flaps extended.

Climbing Turns

During a climbing turn you are concerned with both the rate of climb and the rate of turn. As the rate of climb is dependent on the excess power available, above that required to maintain level flight applying a bank angle will reduce the available excess of power to overcome drag. Therefore if you are to maintain a safe airspeed in the climb, the rate of climb will have to reduce. It will also be necessary to limit the amount of bank angle used.

Slipstream effect will be more pronounced because of the high power setting and comparatively lower airspeed than in the cruise and therefore more rudder pressure will be required to maintain balance. Since you have full power set it is possible that when entering a climbing turn to the left you may need some right rudder pressure. To avoid getting confused about this simply check the balance ball and ensure it is centred in the normal way.

Descending Turns

You may carry out a descending turn from a glide or with power. Banking the aircraft will have reduced the available lift and therefore the rate of descent will increase. The effect of the increase in drag from the banked attitude will also reduce the airspeed therefore it will be necessary to lower the nose attitude to maintain the desired airspeed. It is usual to use 30° of bank in the descending turn as the performance considerations experienced in the climbing turn no longer apply. However, the aircraft may tend to roll out of the turn and aileron will be required to maintain the bank angle.

You will also practise descending turns with partial flap as a prelude to the initial approach to land procedure. Be aware of the increased stalling speed in turns and exercise care, particularly when turning with flap, that you monitor the ASI regularly.

Spiral Descents

A spiral descent with increasing airspeed may occasionally develop from a level or descending turn when either insufficient back pressure or too much bank is applied. Your instructor will give you practice in recovering from such a condition. He or she will deliberately set up a spiral descent and you will notice the steepening angle of bank and increasing airspeed and high rate of descent.

To recover, you should reduce the power (close the throttle if required), roll the wings level and then pitch up to recover from the dive. Only once the speed reduces to a cruise speed, reapply power and climb back up to regain lost altitude. You may experience a small amount of "g" force as you recover from this condition, due to the increased wing loading: see further in Chapter 15.

Compass Turns

Occasionally you may have to use the compass instead of the DI if you suffer a failure of the gyroscopic instruments. The compass is prone to errors which are worst in turning flight. Because of its construction, the magnetic compass will not show the correct heading in a turn, although it can be used to verify the heading once you have rolled level and the compass has been given time to settle down. In order to overcome the errors use a mnemonic to remember:

UNDERSHOOT NORTH OVERSHOOT SOUTH (UNOS)

The errors are not significant when turning through east and west but when turning through north and south under/or over/shoot the heading by 30°. Modify this for headings well removed from north or south. This rule is reversed in the Southern hemisphere when you should overshoot north and undershoot south.

In view of the problems associated with the magnetic compass, it may be preferable to perform a timed rate one turn using a stopwatch based on the formula set out above under **RATE ONE TURNS**.

Example: $\dfrac{\text{Airspeed } (in\ knots) + 7°}{10}$ = required Bank Angle

| 360° | = | 2 minutes | | 90° | = | 30 seconds |
| 180° | = | 1 minute | | 30° | = | 10 seconds |

Quiz No. 9

1. A horizontal force is required in the direction of a turn, to turn the aircraft. This is known as the .... force.
2. A medium level turn is approximately ...... degrees of bank.
3. During a medium level turn, it is necessary to apply a little ...... to maintain altitude.
4. Should you trim the aircraft during the turn?
5. A rate one turn is a heading change of ...... degrees per second.
6. In a climbing turn, the ...... effect is greater and therefore more ...... may be required.
7. When making a turn using the compass, you should .... north, ... south.

Answers
No. 9

1. Centripetal.
2. 30°.
3. Back pressure.
4. No, it is a transient manoeuvre.
5. 3.
6. Slipstream,
   Rudder pressure to balance the aircraft.
7. Undershoot,
   Overshoot.

Chapter 10 - *Part 1*

Slow Flight

Introduction

Slow flight is not an operational exercise: its purpose is to give you the opportunity to learn to recognise the symptoms associated with flying the aircraft at very low speeds close to the stall and to be able to control the aircraft whilst safely restoring it to the correct configuration. You also require the ability to control the aircraft at slow speeds when operating at lower than normal speeds in normal manoeuvres such as just after take-off and in the landing flare. One of the problems that can be encountered in slow speed flight is that when power is being used the aircraft is apt to become unbalanced and this could lead to an unwanted stall, wing drop or even a spin.

The Forces in Slow Flight

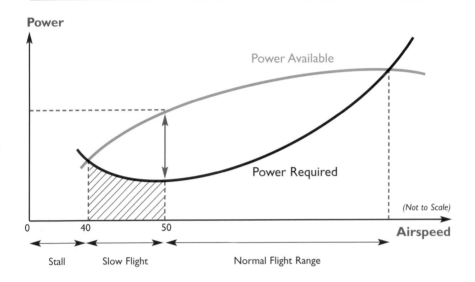

Slow flight is usually defined to mean flight in the range between endurance speed and 5 to 10 knots above the stalling speed. Looking at the power curves illustrated above it can be seen that the minimum power required will mean minimum fuel burn at maximum endurance. In the slow flight range, more power will be required because a higher angle of attack is needed to produce sufficient lift. As the by-product of lift is drag there will be more drag produced and more power will be needed to overcome the extra drag. The aircraft will not be speed stable and a momentary gust or lack of concentration could cause unbalance leading to a loss of control. This is sometimes known as **"flying on the back of the drag curve"**.

Control Effectiveness

You have already experienced the effects of slipstream and airspeed on the controls in exercise 4. You may recall that at low airspeeds the controls felt much less effective or sloppy. You needed larger control deflections to achieve the desired response. The ailerons are particularly ineffective at low speed and the effect of adverse aileron yaw may be more pronounced when rolling into a turn.

If you fly a high wing aircraft then you may experience a change to the effectiveness of the elevator as there can be a dramatic increase in downwash over the tailplane when the aircraft is being flown at a high angle of attack.

The effect of slipstream is likely to be more pronounced, because a higher power setting is being used and therefore the yawing effect on the fin will be increased. Therefore more rudder will be required to maintain balance. Recognition of the condition of slow flight by understanding the control effectiveness and developing the ability to recover the aircraft to safe flight is the main purpose of the exercise.

It is essential to maintain smooth and coordinated use of the controls during the slow flight practice. You need to monitor the airspeed and be aware that flying in the slow flight configuration with a high nose attitude will degrade your ability to maintain a good lookout.

LESSON AIM

To learn to recognise inadvertent slow flight, provide practice in maintaining the aeroplane in balance while returning to normal airspeed.

LESSON OBJECTIVE

By the end of the lesson you will be able to demonstrate safely and correctly your ability to recognise flight at critically low airspeed and return the aeroplane to normal airspeed while maintaining the aeroplane in a balanced state.

AIRMANSHIP

Lookout. Blind Spot. Airspeed Indicator. Controls. **HASELL** Check.

AIR EXERCISE   *Slow Flight, only to be flown with an Instructor Present.*

Teaching Points

Demonstration 1

In straight and level flight (no flap) the nose of the aircraft will be raised, so that the airspeed is 10 kts above the stall.

Symptoms

1) Low airspeed.
2) Higher nose attitude.
3) Controls are less effective.
4) Stall warning may intermittently sound or light, and/or, stay on.

Recovery

1) Increase power (balance) and lower the pitch attitude.
2) Return to straight and level flight.

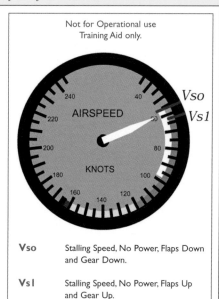

Not for Operational use
Training Aid only.

Vso
Vs1

| Vso | Stalling Speed, No Power, Flaps Down and Gear Down. |
| Vs1 | Stalling Speed, No Power, Flaps Up and Gear Up. |

Demonstration 2	As per demonstration 1, but at 5kts above the stall.
Demonstration 3	As per demonstration 1, with flap applied.
Demonstration 4	As per demonstration 2, with flap applied.
Demonstration 5	15° - 30° of banked turn as per demonstration 1 & 3.
Demonstration 6	Climbing & descending as per demonstration 1 & 3.

HEIGHT • AIRFRAME • SECURITY • ENGINE • LOCATION • LOOKOUT

When you have practised setting up slow flight at airspeeds of 5 and 10 knots above the stall, carried out turns, slow climbs and descents, your instructor will remind you of the go around procedure with flaps down. As previously mentioned, it is in this configuration when you apply full power that there will be the strongest pitch up tendency and this is where it is most likely that the aircraft could stall. Therefore it is essential that you practise the procedure at a safe altitude before having to carry it out in the circuit. Your instructor will probably introduce some distractions whilst you are practising this manoeuvre to show you how easy it is to enter an unwanted slow flight condition inadvertently.

AIRMANSHIP

Although you may not need to carry out a full **"HASELL"** check before practising slow flight it is advisable to consider it, as it is good practice for the Stalling exercise which comes next.

HASELL is a common mnemonic used by pilots as a pre-aerobatic check. In view of the fact that the aircraft could develop some rather unusual attitudes if not correctly recovered from the stall or incipient spin, it is advisable to use this check every time you practise any stalling, slow flight or incipient spin recovery.

H	**HEIGHT**	This should be sufficient to recover at a safe height above the ground, usually 3000 feet.
A	**AIRFRAME**	**CHECK** brakes are off, flaps are set as required.
S	**SECURITY**	Check there are no loose articles in the cockpit, nothing to impede the free movement of the controls. Tighten harnesses and ensure hatches are secure. Cage gyros if possible.
E	**ENGINE**	Mixture should be rich and set carb heat to full hot. Monitor engine temperatures and pressures. Switch on the auxiliary fuel pump and select the fullest tank.
L	**LOCATION**	**ABCD** Clear of; **A**ctive Airfields, **B**uilt up areas, **C**ontrolled Airspace & Clouds & **D**anger areas.
L	**LOOKOUT**	Carry out a clearing turn of 180 degrees or two 90 degree turns to check the area above, below and ahead is clear.

In between each manoeuvre you can carry out an abbreviated **HASELL** check, the **HELL** check.

Left Intentionally Blank

Quiz No. 10a

1.   As you increase drag, more ...... is required.
     This is called flying ...... of the drag curve.

2.   At low airspeeds, the controls feel ......

3.   .... rudder is required to maintain balance at low airspeed.

4.   The mnemonic used before slow flight or stalling is ....

Answers
No. 10a

1. Power, on the back.
2. Less effective or sloppy.
3. More.
4. HASELL

Chapter 10 - *Part 2*

Stalling

Introduction

What is a Stall?

Lift produced by the wing is dependent on the smooth airflow passing over its surface. The amount of lift produced will increase as the angle of attack is increased. When the angle of attack increases the centre of pressure moves forwards until a critical angle of attack of about 15-16° is exceeded. At that point, the boundary layer of air flowing over the wing surface starts to become turbulent and separate from the wing and the centre of pressure moves sharply rearwards, pitching the aircraft nose down.

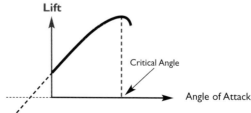

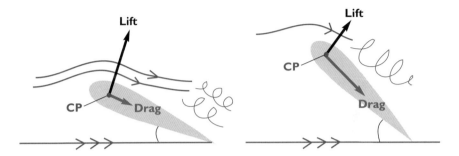

The result of the loss of lift will cause a number of symptoms to occur just prior to the stall and further characteristics at the stall. You will already be familiar with the symptoms associated with slow flight, just before the stall such as the much higher nose attitude, low and decreasing airspeed and sloppy controls. You may have experienced the light buffet of the airframe which you can feel through the controls and you may have heard the stall warner which is usually a bell or horn *(or sometimes a light)* which sounds about 5 to 10 knots before the stall.

At the stall, even though you may have the control column fully back on the stops, the nose of the aircraft will probably drop. There may be a wing drop and there is likely to be a high rate of descent. The only way to recover from this condition is to reduce the angle of attack, i.e. to move the control wheel centrally forwards.

Flying Controls Effectiveness at the Stall

Since there is a reduced airflow over the controls they will be less effective as speed reduces and the stall is approached. Larger movements will be required especially the elevator and rudder. It is the wing that stalls as the fin and tailplane remain unstalled. This is a design feature to ensure that control can be regained by the use of elevator and rudder. In some aircraft the ailerons may become ineffective close to the stall.

Ailerons are normally used to level the wings when one is lower than the other. The problem is that when the control wheel is rotated in the opposite direction to raise a wing, the aileron will deflect downwards on the dropping wing, which will increase the angle of attack on that wing, producing more lift. If the wing is close to the stalling angle of attack then deflection of the aileron could cause that wing to stall which would cause the wing to drop further. If there is any yaw present, a spin could easily ensue.

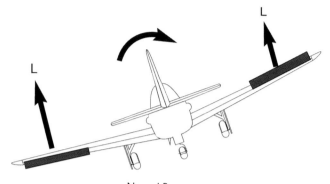

Normal Response

Slow Flight near the Stall

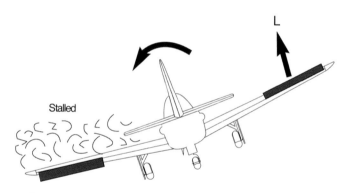

Stalled

Control wheel to right of aeroplane but aeroplane rolls to the **LEFT**

To prevent wing drop *(it is advisable to)* use the rudder to prevent unwanted yaw developing.

Stall Speed

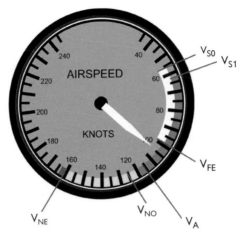

The speed at which an aircraft stalls will vary according to a number of factors, but the stalling will always occur at the same angle of attack. However, since there are no angle of attack indicators on light aircraft, speed is a guide as to when the stall will occur. The basic stall speed is that speed at which the aircraft stalls when it is at maximum weight, with the flaps up, power off and wings level. This speed is called Vs1 and is indicated at the bottom end of the green arc on the ASI. With full flap, the stall speed is Vs0 and is shown at the bottom end of the white arc on the ASI.

Factors Affecting Stalling Speed

Flaps

As flap is lowered the lifting ability of the wings increases. The speed required to maintain level flight reduces and the stall speed will be lower. i.e. Vs0.

Power

When the power is on, the stalling speed will be lower, because a component of the thrust will act upwards to oppose a component of weight. The propeller slipstream also assists by increasing the airflow over the wings, preventing the airflow becoming turbulent and modifying the angle of attack over the centre section of the wing.

Weight

If the weight carried is increased more lift will be required to carry it and therefore at all angles of attack, more airspeed will be needed to provide that extra lift. Thus the stalling speed will be higher if the weight is greater.

Centre of Gravity

If the C of G is further aft, there will be less of a download required on the tailplane and vice versa. The stall speed will be lower with an aft C of G, but the difference with a forward C of G is not very marked within the permitted C of G range.

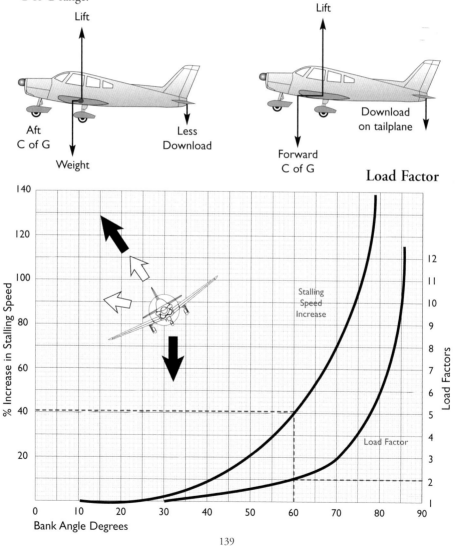

Load Factor

In a turn, the lift must be increased to maintain level flight and therefore the load factor and stall speed will be higher. The increase in lift by increasing angle of attack is felt by the pilot as "**g**". As can be seen from the graph overleaf, as the bank angle increases the "**g**" increases and the stall speed increases dramatically. An accelerated stall or high speed or dynamic stall can occur in situations such as a sudden pull-up to recover from a spiral dive. The stall speed will be much higher and the effects felt at the stall will be much more dramatic.

Contamination of the Wing

The presence of ice or insects on the leading edge of the wing can substantially affect the airflow over the wing leading to the earlier break down of the smooth flow and a stall at a higher speed. Ice can also add significantly to the weight and therefore all ice, frost and other contaminants should be cleaned off the aircraft before flight.

Power Off Stall

Initially you will practise stalls entered from straight and level flight with power off. Note the symptoms as the aircraft approaches the stall. Any of these symptoms can be removed by simply moving the control column forward i.e. reducing the angle of attack. As the aircraft approaches the stall the stall warner will sound and if you continue to increase the back pressure the aircraft will stall.

In order to recover from the stall, reduce the angle of attack by releasing the back pressure, moving the control column centrally forward. Once gliding speed has been achieved and the aircraft is safely flying again, apply full power and climb away. You will notice that there will have been a height loss of 400-500 feet. Do not be in a hurry to climb away as it is possible to experience a secondary stall if you have not given the aircraft long enough to achieve a safe speed. Such a secondary stall may be more violent and a wing drop could occur. If the wing drops, you will not use the aileron to level the wings whilst the aircraft is still stalled as this is likely to aggravate the situation, but use sufficient rudder to prevent further yaw developing.

Once the wings are unstalled you can then roll the wings back to level, and regain lost altitude.

LESSON AIM

To Learn to recognise the symptoms of the stall and how to recover safely/correctly from a stall.

LESSON OBJECTIVE

By the end of the lesson you will be able to demonstrate safely/correctly your ability to recognise the symptoms and causes of the stall. Recover the aeroplane from a stalled condition with the minimum height loss.

AIRMANSHIP

Lookout. Location. Pre-stalling Checks. **HASELL - HELL.**

AIR EXERCISE

Revise Medium Level Turns. To Stall the aeroplane with no Power and no flap, then recovery with and without Power.

Teaching Points

Recovery without Power
Entry:

1) HASELL Checks.
2) Carb. heat, close throttle (balance).
3) Elevator to maintain height.
4) Ailerons neutral near stall speed.

Symptoms of Approaching Stall

1) Airspeed reduces.
2) Controls become less effective, becoming quieter.
3) High nose attitude.
4) Light buffeting - height loss.
5) Stall warning lights and/or sounds.

Symptoms at the Stall

6) Heavy buffeting - height loss.
7) Nose pitches down.
8) Wing may drop.

Recovery:

1) Centrally forward with the control column sufficient to remove buffet and silence stall warner.
2) When gliding airspeed is achieved, carb heat off and apply power to regain altitude.

Note: If wing has dropped prevent further yaw with rudder. When unstalled level the wing with aileron.

Standard Stall Recovery
Recovery with Power:

Entry as before.

Symptoms

As before.

Recovery:

1) Control column centrally forward to remove buffet and silence stall warner. Carb heat off and apply full power; prevent yaw with rudder.
2) If wing has dropped, prevent further yaw with rudder. When unstalled level the wing with aileron.
3) Regain Altitude.

Recovery at Incipient Stage

At the first indication of a stall ie. airspeed reducing, buffet, stall warning activated, poor control response etc. Initiate the appropriate stall recovery technique.

HEIGHT • ENGINE • LOCATION • LOOKOUT

Standard Stall Recovery

Having learnt how to control the aircraft in the stall and to recover by reducing the angle of attack you will then practise the standard stall recovery. You will have realised that the loss of 400 feet or more before control is regained would not be desirable when the aircraft is close to the ground. The addition of power will be used to accelerate the recovery and reduce the loss of height. It will not be necessary to pitch the nose so far forward to unstall the wings as the power will assist. In order to effect the recovery, simultaneously apply full power whilst moving the control column centrally forward. Prevent yaw with rudder and once the wings are unstalled, level them with aileron, centralise the rudder and climb away. Using this technique the loss of height will only be about 50 to 100 feet.

Standard Stall Recovery

• **Simultaneously move the control column centrally forward to unstall the wings AND**
• **Apply full power smoothly opening the throttle and setting carb heat to cold**
• **Prevent yaw or further yaw with rudder**
• **Level the wings with aileron if necessary**
• **Achieve safe flying speed and adopt climb**

Recovery at the Incipient Stage

Clearly it would be preferable not to stall the aircraft at all and having practised recognition of the symptoms, recoveries without power and the Standard Stall Recovery technique, you will now learn how to recover at the incipient stage i.e. before the aircraft has stalled. The main difference between this technique and the Standard Stall Recovery is that you will not wait for the wings to stall but recognise by the warning sound of the stall warner and onset of the buffet that the stall is imminent and recover at that point. Since the wings are not actually stalled the movement of the control column required is much less. It should be possible to recover without any loss of height at all.

Quasi-Stall

This situation may occur if the aircraft is in a semi-stalled condition. You could experience this during a mislanding where the aircraft is allowed to balloon or bounce and becomes airborne at a very low speed, perhaps with flaps down. If the situation is allowed to develop, a high rate of sink can occur resulting in a heavy impact with the runway. Clearly not a very desirable state of affairs! The problem is that the aircraft may not appear to be stalled but the controls will be sloppy and a high sink rate will give you the clue. Early application of full power will minimise the danger.

Effect of Power

If a stall is set up with power on, the effect of the slipstream will delay the stall especially on the inner sections of the wing. The elevator and rudder will be more effective but the aircraft will be more likely to drop a wing at the stall. Use the Standard Stall Recovery technique preventing further yaw with rudder. You will notice a higher nose attitude, a lower stalling speed and more likelihood of wing drop in a power on stall.

LESSON AIM

To Learn to recognise the symptoms and causes of the stall in approach configuration and how to recover safely/correctly from a stall.

LESSON OBJECTIVE

By the end of the lesson you will be able to recognise the symptoms and causes of the stall. Recover the aeroplane from a stalled condition in different flight configurations with the minimum height loss.

AIRMANSHIP

Lookout. Location. Pre-stalling Checks. **HASELL - HELL.**

AIR EXERCISE

Revise Climb, Clean Stall. To Stall the aeroplane in various flight configurations **with** *and* **without** *Power.*

Teaching Points

a) Stalling with No Power and with Flap
(eg. Glide Approach)

Symptoms
1) Airspeed reduces rapidly.
2) Lower nose attitude.
3) Lower stalling airspeed.
4) More pronounced stall symptoms.

Recovery:
Standard Recovery Technique.

b) Stalling with Power and No Flap
(eg. Flapless Approach)

Symptoms
1) Airspeed reduces slowly.
2) Higher nose attitude.
3) Lower stalling airspeed.
4) More pronounced stall.

Recovery:
Standard Recovery Technique.

HEIGHT • ENGINE • LOCATION • LOOKOUT

c) Stalling with Power and with Flap
(eg. Powered Approach)

Symptoms
1) Airspeed reducing normally.
2) Normal nose attitude.
3) Lower stalling airspeed.
4) More pronounced stall.

Recovery:
Standard Recovery Technique.
Then raise flap in stages to climb away.
Completed correctly, height loss will be minimal in configuration a, b & c.

d) Stalling with Power on & Approach Flap in turn using 20° bank
(approx.) (eg. Base turn to final)
Note: Wing may drop either direction.

Recovery:
Standard Recovery Technique and as before raise flap in stages.

e) Recovery at Incipient Stage
At the first indication of a stall ie. airspeed reducing, buffet, stall warning activated, poor control response etc. Initiate the appropriate stall recovery technique.

Effect of Flap

The lateral stability of the aircraft reduces with flap extended due to the changed distribution of the lift over the wing. Additionally the increased lift produced by lowering flaps will lead to a lower stalling speed, but the entry to the stall will be rapid as the speed will reduce very quickly when the power is reduced. The effectiveness of the controls will be lost sooner. Use the Standard Stall Recovery technique but a greater control movement may be required to effect full recovery. Flaps should be raised in stages.

Stall in Approach Configuration

Stalling with power and flaps simulates the approach to land and it is necessary to practise this in order to appreciate the amount and rate of control movement needed to achieve a rapid recovery. The nose attitude at the stall will be higher, the stall speed lower and a much more pronounced stall may be experienced with a far greater likelihood of a wing drop. Having practised this using the Standard Stall Recovery technique you will then practise recovering at the incipient stage as allowing a stall to develop on final approach would not give you enough height to recover. Thus it is essential to take early action to avoid such a dangerous situation developing.

Stalling in the Turn

Again the aircraft will be set up in the initial approach or base leg configuration and the turn onto final approach simulated. With power and flap and in the turn, the higher "g" loading experienced in the turn may lead very quickly to a significant wing drop at the stall. Attempting to level the wing with aileron would aggravate the situation and possibly lead to a spin. Prompt recovery using the Standard Stall Recovery technique must be used only rolling the wings level once the wings are unstalled, again raising the flap in stages, and regaining height loss.

The Departure Stall

Stalling in the climb at full power could occur on take off if the nose attitude is not selected correctly. If there is an imbalance, the uncompensated yaw will lead to a dramatic wing drop and the strong possibility of a spin which could be unrecoverable if at low altitude just after departure. The other feature is the very steep nose attitude at the stall. Clearly this can be avoided by selecting the correct climbing attitude and preventing yaw or further yaw after attaining and monitoring the climb speed following the take off.

AIRMANSHIP   HASELL and HELL!

Quiz No. 106

1. A stall is caused when the .... of ...... is exceeded.

2. The symptoms of the stall include: ......, ..., ..., ... and ......

3. At the stall, the wing may drop. This can be prevented by use of ......

4. A number of factors affect stalling speed. These include: ......, ..., ..., ... of ......, ... and ......

5. Recovery from the stall can be effected simply by moving the control column forward. This leads to a large ......

6. To reduce the altitude loss at the stall, use the .... technique.

7. To achieve minimum height loss, ... at the ....

8. If power is on at the stall, a wing drop is ...... likely.

9. Stalling with flaps down leads to reduction of ....

Left Intentionally Blank

Answers
No. 10b

1. Critical angle, attack.
2. Higher nose attitude, Lowering Airspeed, Sloppy Controls, Buffet, Stall Warner.
3. Rudder.
4. Power, Flaps, Weight, Centre Gravity, Load Factor, Wing Contamination.
5. Loss of Altitude.
6. Standard Stall Recovery.
7. Recover, Incipient Stage.
8. More.
9. Lateral Stability.

Chapter 11 - Exercise 11

Spinning & Spin Avoidance

Introduction

Spinning is not a compulsory part of the PPL syllabus, but spin avoidance is and therefore it is important to understand how and when an aircraft gets into a spin and how to recognise the symptoms and recover before the spin condition develops.

What is a Spin?

A spin is a condition of stalled flight in which the aircraft describes a spiral descent. During the spin the aircraft will be simultaneously pitching, rolling and yawing i.e. in motion about all three axes until recovery is effected by the pilot. The aircraft will be rapidly losing height but the airspeed may be very low, and fluctuating.

Causes of a Spin and How it Develops

We have already seen that at the stall a wing may drop. Usually this is because of imbalance and yaw developing close to the stall. Only a small amount of yaw will need to exist for the amount of lift being produced by one wing to alter relative to the other. This differential will lead to a slight rolling action and the lowering wing will develop a higher angle of attack than the rising wing causing it to stall. It will drop more quickly, becoming more stalled and producing more drag; it will yaw towards the downgoing wing. The upgoing wing will be producing more lift than the downgoing wing and therefore less drag and a condition known as autorotation will tend to develop.

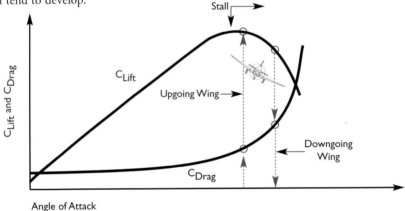

The position of the C of G will affect the aeroplane's characteristics in the spin. If it is rearwards the spin will be flatter and the rate of rotation may decrease. However, it will be harder to recover from a flat spin as the amount of forward control pressure required to unstall the wings will be that much greater. The converse is a forward C of G where the aircraft is in a much steeper attitude, but this makes it easier to recover from the spin and may even prevent the entry in the first place as the aircraft will be more likely to go into a spiral dive than a spin.

At the incipient stage of the stall, if power is on it may lead to an even greater tendency for the wing to drop, which could lead to a spin developing. Once in the spin, power will also destabilise the aeroplane as the slipstream over the outer wing will increase lift and consequently roll, thereby increasing the rotation. In order to recover therefore it is essential to ensure that the throttle is closed.

The effect of flap will also cause problems for recovery as flaps tend to reduce the effectiveness of the rudder and elevator, by blanking. They should be retracted before attempting the recovery.

Pre-Spinning Checks

You need to check in the **POH** that the aircraft is cleared for intentional spinning, that the C of G is within the correct limits and ensure that you are familiar with the correct technique for the recovery from the spin for the aircraft. Spinning, even with recovery at the incipient stage is classed as an aerobatic manoeuvre and therefore you should carry out a full **HASELL** check. Calculate the height at which to start the manoeuvre which will enable you to recover the aircraft to normal flight no lower than 3000 feet, a.g.l. noting that each rotation of the aircraft may consume 400 to 500 feet.

Incipient Spin – Symptoms and Recovery

At the incipient stage of the spin, the wing will have dropped following the stall. The most important action is to ensure that the controls are centralised. Once the aircraft has recovered from the stall use the controls to return to your normal flight path in a coordinated manner and add full power to regain altitude.

Full Spin – Symptoms and Recovery

In training it is normally necessary to induce the spin entry by deliberately introducing a large amount of yaw close to the stall. This will be effected by applying full rudder in the desired spin direction whilst moving the control column fully back. Avoid using aileron as this will reduce the rudder effectiveness.

In addition to the steep nose down attitude, there will be a continuous rotation, low airspeed, rapid loss of height and possibly buffet.

The standard spin recovery technique should be used:
- Check throttle closed and flaps up
- Verify direction of spin
- Apply full opposite rudder
- Pause
- Move the control column centrally forward to unstall the wings (may need to go all the way forward)
- When the rotation stops, centralise the controls
- Level the wings and ease out of the dive
- Raise the nose above the horizon and apply full power to climb back up to altitude. *Note: always check POH before spins as spin entry and recovery may not be standard.*

Spiral Dive

Due to the design characteristics of certain aircraft, they are reluctant to enter or maintain a spin and may instead develop into a spiral dive. In the latter, the characteristic which is most notably different is the rapidly increasing airspeed. The recovery technique is set out in Chapter 15.

Exercise 11 — Spin Avoidance

LESSON AIM
To Learn to recognise the symptoms and causes of the incipient spin.

LESSON OBJECTIVE
By the end of the lesson you will be able to demonstrate safely/correctly your ability to recognise the symptoms and causes of the incipient spin. Recover the aeroplane from an incipient spin with the minimum height loss.

AIRMANSHIP
Lookout. Location. Pre-spin Checks. **HASELL**

AIR EXERCISE — *Incipient Spin and Recovery Technique.*

Teaching Points

Symptoms
As for stall but with significant wing drop.

Entry
1) Lookout - **HASELL** checks
2) Enter as for the stall.
3) Just before the stall, apply rudder in the direction you wish the incipient spin to occur.
4) Nose drops, wing drops rapidly.

Recovery:
1) Centralise all controls: if nose attitude significantly below horizon, close throttle.
2) Centrally forward with the control column, until buffet stops.
3) Level wings.
4) Carb heat to cold - apply full power.
5) Regain altitude.
6) Return to normal flight.

To prevent too much height loss, the recovery should be completed quickly.

Quiz No. 11

1. In a spin the aircraft is ...... and simultaneously ......, ... and ......

2. Autorotation occurs when the ...... wing is producing more ..... than the downgoing wing.

3. If you intend to spin the aircraft you should check the ...... and that the ...... is within limits.

4. In the standard spin recovery, the first action is to .... and ....

Answers
No. 11

1. Stalled, Pitching, Rolling, Yawing.
2. Upgoing, Lift.
3. POH, C of G.
4. Check Throttle Closed, Flaps Up.

Chapter 12 - *Exercise 12*

Take Off & Climb to the Downwind Position

12. LESSON AIM

To learn safely and correctly to take off and climb the aeroplane to the downwind position.

LESSON OBJECTIVE

By the end of the lesson you will be able to demonstrate safely and correctly your ability to do this, at the correct height and spacing.

AIRMANSHIP

Lookout. R/T. Airfield Procedures. Altimeter Setting. Landing Checks. Surface Wind and Runway Conditions.

Introduction

There are a number of factors to consider during the initial acceleration and roll as well as during the actual take-off and climb. These matters are conveniently grouped together under the heading of Aircraft Performance. Take off distance required and take off run need to be calculated both of which will be altered by the factors listed below. The take-off run is the distance the aeroplane travels until it becomes airborne. The take-off distance is the distance measured over the ground to the point at which the aircraft has reached a height of 50 feet.

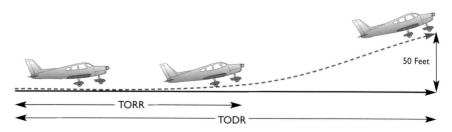

Forces during Take-off

During the take-off the aircraft must be accelerated to a lift-off speed. This is usually calculated as 1.15 times the stalling speed. The thrust produced by the engine has to overcome the inertia of the stationary aeroplane and the drag and rolling resistance of the tyres on the runway. Once airborne, the excess thrust over drag will provide the initial climb rate to clear obstacles.

Use of Controls

Elevator

As the aircraft starts to accelerate apply a little back pressure to the control column to take some of the weight off the nosewheel. Do not lift off too early as the aircraft may become airborne in a semi-stalled condition and a gust could cause the stall and a loss of control. Keeping the nosewheel on the ground too long is also undesirable as it will lead to a tendency to "wheelbarrow". This causes unnecessary stresses and sideforces on the nosewheel which could weaken it and lead to damage on landing.

Rudder

Use rudder to maintain directional control during the take-off roll. As the power is smoothly increased, more rudder will be required.

Power

The use of power gives rise to a number of factors which affect the take-off:

- **Torque reaction**
- **Slipstream effect**
- **Gyroscopic effect**
- **Asymmetric blade effect**

1. **Torque Reaction:**

    As the propeller rotates in one direction, the effect of engine torque *(simply a twisting motion)* causes the aircraft to want to rotate in the opposite direction. This is most pronounced during take-off and is experienced as more pressure on one mainwheel than the other, resulting in yaw. The direction of yaw depends on the direction the propeller is turning. Normally training aeroplanes are equipped with propellers which turn clockwise when viewed from behind *(in the pilot's seat)* and thus the yaw effect is to the left;

2. Slipstream Effect:

You have already seen the effect of slipstream in Exercise 4. As you will recall the effect is most noticeable at high propeller rpm and low speed, thus at the start of the take-off roll these factors are greatest. The slipstream corkscrew is very tight and causes most yaw, which will need to be counteracted with rudder.

3. Gyroscopic Effect:

The rotation of the propeller is similar to the operation of a gyroscope and exhibits the same characteristics, of rigidity and precession *(see volume 4 for more detail on the operation of gyroscopes)*. If a force is applied to the rim of the propeller's plane of rotation, the resultant force will be experienced 90 degrees from the point of application and in the direction of rotation. This will be felt as a pitching action and a yawing motion. Both rudder and elevator will be required to prevent the undesirable effects of this. *(This is mainly the problem of tail draggers)*

4. Asymmetric Blade Effect:

This effect is only significant in tailwheel aircraft as the plane of rotation of the propeller is at a high angle of attack which exacerbates the swing or yaw tendency on the take-off roll.

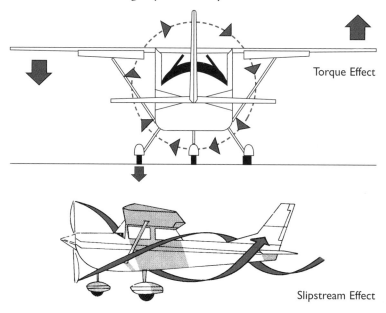

Torque Effect

Slipstream Effect

Factors Affecting Take-off Distance

Wind

If there is a headwind, the aircraft will reach take-off speed at a lower ground speed and a reduced take-off run will be required. A tailwind has an adverse effect on take-off run and climb out angle. A crosswind will give a side force on the keel surface leading to a further tendency to yaw during the take-off run *(in addition to the 4 factors listed above)*. Crosswind take-offs are dealt with in Chapter 13 in connection with crosswind circuits.

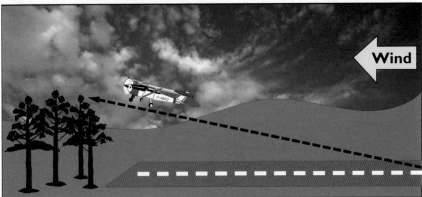

Flap

The use of flap during take-off will lower the stalling speed and therefore the lift-off speed will be lower. This will also reduce the length of the take-off run but does not usually reduce the take-off distance required as the climb rate will be reduced.

Ground Surface and Gradient

Soft surfaces such as grass which has been soaked by a long rainy spell, will significantly increase the rolling friction thus the take-off run will increase. Long wet grass may increase the distance by 50%. The surface is also a factor as a rutted uneven surface could lead to the aircraft becoming airborne at too low a speed and then impacting the runway heavily, causing damage. The slope or gradient of the runway can be significant. An upslope will increase the take-off run and a downslope will decrease it.

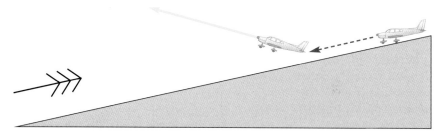

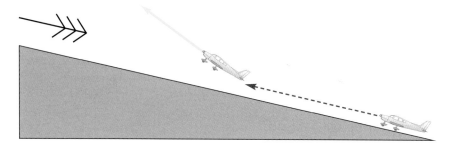

Weight, Altitude and Temperature

You will recall from chapter 10, that increasing the weight of the aircraft by 10% will increase the stalling speed by 5% which means the lift-off speed will also be increased by 5%. Weight increase will also mean a larger mass to accelerate and an increased inertia. The increased take-off run for a 5% increase in weight could be as much as 25%.

The effect of temperature and altitude defines **"Density Altitude"** and this can have an effect on performance. Increasing density altitude will increase the take-off speed required and lead to a reduced amount of available engine power. An increase in density altitude of 1000 feet or a temperature increase of 10°C above International Standard Atmosphere (ISA) 15°C will result in an increased take-off run of 10%.

Note: a factor of 1.33% should be applied for safety to the total.

Pre-take Off Checks

It is important to use the approved checklist to carry out the checks before taking off. Each aircraft will be different and it is essential to ensure that the checks are actioned when called out, not merely recited by rote. Any doubt or concern about the functioning of any item of equipment, systems or services should lead to the question **"should I take-off?"** If you are in doubt, it is better to seek assistance from a mechanic than to launch into the air and then discover the engine is not developing full power. Your instructor will explain how to carry out each check and the purpose of it as well as any specific parameters you should look for and any warning signs that would indicate that all is not well.

The Take-off

After receiving clearance from air traffic control, ensure that the approach path is clear of traffic *(even if air traffic control has given you a clearance you should always do this as part of good airmanship, as there could be a non-radio aircraft or other unexpected phenomenon).* Then roll onto the runway and ensure that the aircraft is straight and that you are using all of the available runway. Check that the DI and compass are aligned and that the reading is sensible for the runway e.g. 260 ± 5° runway 26.

Select a reference point ahead in order to maintain a straight path during the take-off run. Release the brakes and ensure that your heels are on the floor, well away from the brakes to prevent inadvertent use during the acceleration. Smoothly apply full power opening up the throttle to a count of three.

Checks during the Take-off

During the take-off roll, check that the engine gauges are reading steadily in the green and that full power (**rpm**) is developing. As the aircraft starts to accelerate, keep straight with rudder, ease the weight off the nosewheel and check the ASI to ensure that the airspeed is registering and increasing. When you reach lift-off speed, smoothly lift off using elevator. Once the aircraft is airborne just check forward very slightly to prevent too much pitch up as this will also enable the aircraft to accelerate to the climb speed. If you experience any abnormal instrument indications or poor acceleration, then abandon the take-off. *(see later in this chapter for emergencies during and after take-off)*

Exercise 12 Take-Off & Climb to Downwind Position

LESSON AIM

To learn safely and correctly to take-off and climb the aeroplane to a downwind position.

LESSON OBJECTIVE

By the end of the lesson you will be able to demonstrate safely and correctly your ability to take-off and climb the aeroplane to a downwind position, at the correct height and spacing.

AIRMANSHIP

Lookout. R/T. Airfield Procedures. Altimeter Setting. Landing Checks. Surface Wind and Runway Conditions.

AIR EXERCISE   *Take-off, Climb, Cross Wind Leg and Down Wind Leg.*

Teaching Points

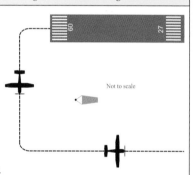

Not to scale

Pre Take-Off

1) Taxy Checks.
2) Power Checks.
3) Vital Actions/Pre Take-Off Checks.
4) RT Call.

Take-Off

1) Aeroplane straight with runway centre line.
2) Check DI/Compass, pick visual reference point.
3) Smoothly apply full power, keep straight with rudder.
4) Ailerons (into wind, if necessary) and elevator neutral.
5) Check power (RPM), T's & P's airspeed. Take weight off nosewheel.
6) At the correct airspeed apply back pressure to lift off cleanly, accelerate to climb speed.
7) Adopt a climbing attitude and select a new reference point, to maintain climb.

Climb Out and Cross Wind Leg

1) Maintain runway centre line and counter any drift.
2) At 200-300ft check **F**laps, **E**ngine T & P's, **A**ttitude and **T**rim (F.E.A.T.).
3) At 500ft select a feature, lookout, climbing turn onto the cross wind leg.
4) Look back at the runway, counter any drift, at circuit height level off.

Downwind Leg

1) Lookout, pick feature.
2) Turn downwind, check heading.
3) Maintain circuit height and parallel to runway (feature).
4) RT Call, abeam upwind end of runway.
5) Landing Checks.

After Take-Off Checks

Once you have reached a safe altitude, at least 300 feet a.g.l. retract any flap used for take-off. Check that you are maintaining a straight climb out path and correcting as necessary for any wind drift, ensure that the engine gauges are still steady in the green and trim off any pressures for the climb. Remember to keep the lookout going in the climb. If your aircraft has a fuel pump fitted then switch it off at 1000 feet a.g.l. (if leaving the circuit) and *(if fitted)* monitor the fuel pressure gauge and fuel flow.

Climbing to the Downwind Position

In the circuit you will commence a climbing turn onto crosswind at approximately 500 to 600 feet to track at right angles to the take-off path. Continue the climb, using a reference feature to one side of the nose to keep straight and level off at circuit height. Normally this is at 1000 feet a.g.l. but there are variations between 750 feet and 1200 feet depending on airspace restrictions or noise sensitive areas. Your levelling off should use the standard technique for levelling off from a climb i.e. A-P-T.

Normal Circuit Pattern

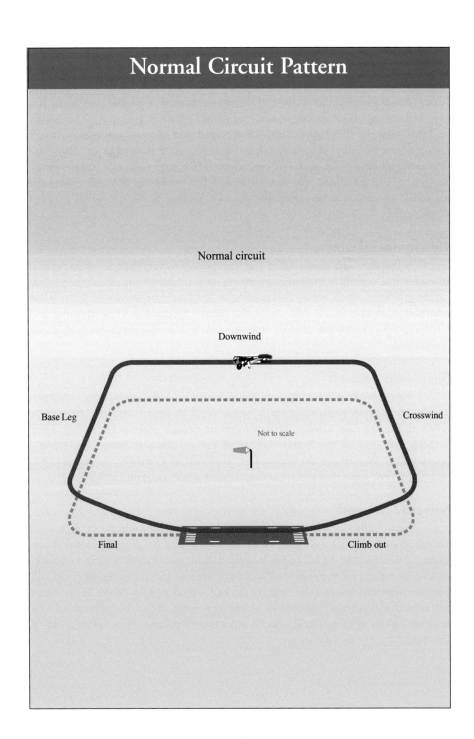

Normal circuit

Downwind

Base Leg

Crosswind

Not to scale

Final

Climb out

Once you are correctly positioned relative to the runway *(in the 45 degree position)*, make a 30° level banked turn onto the Downwind leg, again picking a reference feature to ensure that you track straight and parallel to the runway. It is better to make medium level turns in the circuit as there is a blind spot when you turn and the use of 30° instead of rate 1 turns will minimise the time spent turning and incurring the blind spot. Lookout is a vital part of good airmanship in the circuit where a number of aircraft will be operating quite close together. Also good circuit discipline is essential to safe operations. Make your radio call "**downwind**" as soon as you are abeam the upwind end of the runway as this will enable the air traffic controller to sequence the flow of landing traffic according to their relative speed.

Crosswind Take-off

When there is a crosswind, it will be necessary to vary the take-off technique to ensure that control is maintained throughout the take-off run. Raise the aileron on the side from which the wind is coming by holding the control wheel into wind returning it to the neutral position as the aircraft accelerates. Once airborne and climbing, turn the aircraft slightly into wind to enable the climb-out path to be maintained.

Short-field Take-off

This procedure should be used when there is an obstruction in the climb-out path or the runway available is rough or restricted in length such as a farm strip. Select the appropriate amount of flap for your aircraft *(refer to the POH)*. Then keeping your feet on the brakes, apply full power, check all gauges are reading normally and then release the brakes. Lift off cleanly and establish the initial climb with flaps, *(best angle of climb)* retracting them at a safe speed and height.

Soft-field Take-off

Again using flap will be an advantage. The main point in this case is that the aircraft should be kept rolling in order to prevent it from bogging down if the surface is very muddy. As full power is applied, bring the control column well back, to take the weight off the nosewheel but once the speed increases the elevators will become more effective and the nose should be lowered slightly. As the lift increases the aircraft will become airborne at a very low speed. Again the nose should be lowered slightly to allow the aircraft to accelerate in ground effect before entering the climb.

Chapter 12 - *Exercise 12E*

Emergencies on Take-Off

LESSON AIM
To learn safely and correctly the Emergency Procedures for Take-Off.

LESSON OBJECTIVE
By the end of the lesson you will be able to demonstrate safely and correctly your ability to abandon a take-off and the procedures to adopt with an engine failure after take-off.

AIRMANSHIP
Lookout. R/T. Crash Drills. Checklist for Aircraft Type.

AIR EXERCISE   *Action when the engine fails.*

Teaching Points

1) Abandoned Take-Off before rotation with sufficient runway remaining.

2) Abandoned Take-Off before rotation with insufficient runway remaining.

3) Engine Failure after rotation with sufficient runway remaining.

4) Engine Failure after rotation with insufficient runway remaining.

5) Crash Drills.

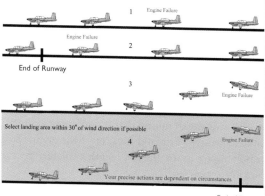

165

Abandoned Take-off

If the engine misfires, runs roughly or fails to develop normal power during the take-off roll, the throttle should be closed and the take-off abandoned. There may be other overwhelming reasons for abandoning the take-off such as a door or window coming open, the seat slipping back or an obstruction such as an animal walking onto the runway. In all cases after closing the throttle, keep the aircraft straight, apply firm braking and bring the aircraft to a stop. Summon assistance and then shut down the engine if necessary.

Engine Failure after Take-off (EFATO)

The options available to the pilot faced with this emergency will depend on the height already gained and the availability of clear areas ahead. A prompt decision as to how to handle the problem is vital. The most important action is to lower the nose immediately to maintain flying speed. Adopt the glide. Then you need to select a landing area which is as clear as possible of obstructions and preferably into wind. Turn no more than is necessary to reach a safe landing area. **DO NOT ATTEMPT A LOW LEVEL TURN BACK TO THE FIELD** (unless no other option remains). Ensure that the throttle is closed as you do not want the engine to come back to life temporarily as this would be a distraction which could lead to a stall and uncontrolled crash instead of a controlled landing from which you should walk away unhurt.

If you have sufficient height transmit a short **MAYDAY** call and it is sensible to set the mixture to idle cut-off, turn off the fuel and magnetos, tighten the harnesses and unlatch the doors. Use flap to ensure the landing is made at as slow a speed as possible, turning off the Master switch when flap has been selected.

After landing, stop the aircraft and close down any remaining services. Evacuate the aircraft *(in case it catches fire)*.

It is worth noting that if you are operating off a long runway you may have sufficient runway to land back on if the engine stops after rotation. This is a good reason always to use the full length available, as "runway behind you is as useless as fuel in the bowser!"

Quiz No. 12

1. During the take off it is a good idea to apply a little ...... to the control column to take some of the ...... off the nosewheel.

2. The effect of power causes a number of factors during the take-off: ......, ..., ... and ......

3. Take-off distance is affected by: (select correct answer)

    a. Headwind or Tailwind
    b. Use of Flap
    c. Ground Surface and Gradient
    d. Weight, altitude and Temperature

    1) a, b, c.
    2) b, c, d.
    3) all of the above.

4. The climbing turn onto crosswind is commenced at approximately ...... feet above ground level.

5. To achieve a short-field take off, it is usual to select ...... before applying ...... power.

6. In the event of an engine failure after take-off, the most important action is to ......

Answers
No. 12

1. Back Pressure, Weight.
2. Torque Reaction, Slipstream Effect, Gyroscopic Effect, Asymmetric Blade Effect.
3. 3).
4. 500.
5. Flap, Full.
6. Lower the nose of the aircraft.

Chapter 13 - Exercise 13

Circuit, Approach & Landing

13. LESSON AIM

To learn to fly the circuit safely and correctly, to make a powered approach and landing.

LESSON OBJECTIVE

By the end of the lesson you will be able to demonstrate safely and correctly your ability to fly the circuit, approach and land on the active runway.

AIRMANSHIP

Lookout. R/T. Airfield procedures. Altimeter setting. Aeroplane checks. Surface wind and runway conditions.

Introduction

When you start flying in the circuit all of the manoeuvres you have been practising in the local area suddenly come together and initially you will find the workload is very high as you try to fly accurately, maintain a good lookout at a time when the airspace around you is very busy and additionally you have to make the correct radio calls at the appropriate points. It may also seem frustrating at first that you can fly reasonably tidily around the circuit but then it all goes wrong in the last few seconds of the landing. It is worth remembering that it is very important to fly a well-judged circuit with a good understanding of what the wind is doing to you, as **A GOOD LANDING FOLLOWS A GOOD APPROACH AND A GOOD APPROACH FOLLOWS A GOOD CIRCUIT.** There are a number of different techniques to learn for the approach but to start with you will need to learn the normal powered approach.

The Circuit Pattern - Positioning (see circuit pattern on Page 163)

Circuit patterns are normally left-hand, unless there is a conflicting requirement such as a built-up area or noise sensitive zones which may dictate a right-hand circuit. It is easier for the pilot, sitting on the left to make left-hand circuits. In the UK, circuits are normally flown at a height of 1000 feet measured on the QFE *(to give height above aerodrome on the altimeter)*. Normally you will land into a headwind where possible, as the groundspeed will be lower and there will be better directional control and a shorter landing distance.

Once you have positioned downwind and made your **"downwind"** call on the radio, you should carry out your pre-landing checks. These will be set out in your checklist, but you should commit these checks to memory, as now is not the time to be looking inside at the checklist. Do not simply recite the checks by rote, but touch and, where necessary, action the items on the list. Each aircraft will have slightly different checks, but they are likely to include:

Brakes	Check there is pressure and that they are off.
Undercarriage	Down (in a fixed gear aircraft you do not need to include this check)
Mixture	Should now be set to rich.
Fuel	Change to the fuller tank (or both tanks) and select fuel pump on if fitted.
Instruments	Check everything is indicating correctly in the green arcs.
Carburettor Heat	Check for ice.
Hatches & Harnesses	Secure.

The mnemonic for the above checks is **BUMFICH**.

LESSON AIM

To learn safely and correctly the Circuit, Powered Approach and Landing.

LESSON OBJECTIVE

By the end of the lesson you will be able to demonstrate safely and correctly your ability to fly the circuit, approach and land onto the active runway.

AIRMANSHIP

Lookout. R/T. Airfield Procedures. Altimeter Setting. Landing Checks. Surface Wind and Runway Conditions.

AIR EXERCISE   *Base Leg, Final Approach and Landing.*

Teaching Points

Base Leg

1) When 45° beyond the runway threshold, commence a turn onto base leg, allow for drift.
2) Approximately half way along the base leg reduce power (apply carb heat) and select the appropriate amount of flap, maintain airspeed and trim.
3) Maintain a good lookout.
4) Anticipate runway centre line and turn final, aim to be at 500 ft AAL.

Final Approach

1) Select reference point for landing.
2) Maintain approach with a combination of elevator to maintain speed. Aileron and rudder for direction and power to adjust the rate of descent.
3) RT Call.
4) At 300ft depending on aeroplane type, wind conditions and stipulations in the owners/pilots manual, further flap may be added.

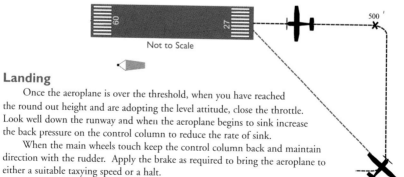

Not to Scale

Landing

Once the aeroplane is over the threshold, when you have reached the round out height and are adopting the level attitude, close the throttle. Look well down the runway and when the aeroplane begins to sink increase the back pressure on the control column to reduce the rate of sink.

When the main wheels touch keep the control column back and maintain direction with the rudder. Apply the brake as required to bring the aeroplane to either a suitable taxying speed or a halt.

Turning onto Base Leg

The turn onto base leg should be made when the aircraft is at the 45-degree *(or "eight o'clock")* position from the runway threshold. It is important to choose this point on the runway as there may be a displaced threshold *(marked by an arrow)* and aiming simply for the end of the runway would cause you to undershoot and possibly hit an obstruction. Once the turn *(which should be a medium level 30° banked turn)* is completed, set up the initial approach configuration, by applying full carburettor heat, reducing power and selecting flap as required *(generally about half flap)*. Trim the aircraft and maintain a stable airspeed.

Turning onto Final Approach

Anticipate the effect of the wind and make a medium descending turn to roll out onto the final approach path aligned with the runway centreline, aiming to be lined up by 500 feet a.g.l. Adjust the bank angle to coincide with the interception of the runway centreline *(but not more than 35° bank)*. Once established on final approach, call **"final"** to obtain your clearance to land or touch and go. If you are not cleared because of an aircraft ahead of you or an obstruction on the runway *(other reasons are set out later)* then you should execute a **"missed approach"** or **"go around"** *(see later in this chapter)*.

Judging the effect of the wind is vitally important when you are close to the ground. If you have a tailwind on base leg you need to turn onto final approach a little sooner as otherwise you may end up flying past the centreline and needing to turn back onto final. The temptation can be to tighten up the turn which is inadvisable so close to the ground and already configured with flaps at a slow speed. As the bank angle increases so does the stall speed and the chance of a stall/spin increases, from which recovery would be difficult at low altitude.

A crosswind on final approach will require you to crab the approach *(see later under section on crosswind circuits)*. Near to the ground there is often a lot more turbulence from surface friction and windshear, which can cause violent fluctuations in your airspeed. If you encounter such conditions and your approach becomes unstable it would be best to make a go around and try again, as on the second attempt, you will anticipate the effect and be ready to make the necessary corrections with power. It may also be better to make the approach using less flap in very turbulent or gusty conditions.

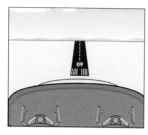
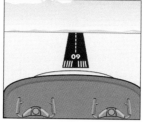
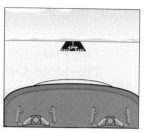

| Too High | Good Approach | Too Low |

Try to judge the perspective of the runway as early as possible in the approach so that you can control your approach path better. Pick an aiming point and keep it in a fixed position in the windscreen. Control your airspeed with elevator and your rate of descent with power. If the aiming point is moving up the windscreen you are getting too low so add a little power to reduce the rate of descent. If your aiming point is moving down, then you are too high so reduce the power to increase the rate of descent. Remember that

Power + Attitude = Performance

So if you have had to add power you will also need to adjust the attitude to maintain the airspeed i.e. raise the nose slightly. The opposite is also true – reducing power, adjust the nose attitude by lowering it slightly. Keep the aircraft trimmed accurately and flying the approach will be easier. Keep your right hand on the throttle to be ready to make any small power adjustments and keep your left hand on the control wheel to enable small elevator control inputs to be made.

In some aircraft you will select full flap on the final approach so remember to retrim after the final selection of flap. Normally you will make continual small adjustments on the approach as the effect of the wind alters as you descend.

The final part of the approach is often referred to as the **"short final"** and if you have been asked by air traffic control to **"continue"** because of another aircraft ahead, you may well call again to confirm you are on short final to obtain your clearance to land. The carburettor heat should be returned to the cold position at about 200 to 300 feet in case you need to execute a go around *(as otherwise you would not achieve maximum power with the throttle fully open).*

The Landing

- **The Flare**
- **The Hold-Off**
- **The Touchdown**
- **The Landing Roll**

Once the aircraft arrives over the threshold at approximately 20 feet, you will enter the flare or round out. This is achieved by changing the descending attitude into a level attitude. You should gradually reduce the power as you gradually adjust the nose attitude. The aircraft will start to sink as the throttle is closed and you will need to increase the backpressure on the control column. Now hold the aircraft off by progressively increasing the backpressure as if trying to keep the aircraft in the air for as long as possible. Look down to the far end of the runway and when the aircraft touches down, the mainwheels should contact the ground first and as gently as possible. Ideally the aircraft should be just at the point of stall so you may hear the stall warner going. Keep the nosewheel off the ground for as long as possible until the aircraft has slowed down and then gently lower it onto the ground, maintaining directional control, with rudder. Use brakes if necessary to slow the aircraft down and clear the active runway as directed by air traffic control. The landing is only complete once the landing roll is complete.

Most people find it hard to judge the flare and hold-off. Try not to look over the nose of the aircraft, as this will prevent you from gaining a proper perspective of the aircraft in relation to the ground. The high nose attitude will restrict your forward visibility and affect judgment of height off the ground. Look far enough ahead to give you depth perception and slightly to the left of the nose to prevent you flying the aircraft into the ground nosewheel first.

After Landing Checks

The aircraft should be taxied clear of the active runway and stopped. Using the checklist, carry out the required actions – usually check flaps are retracted, carburettor heat is set to cold, fuel pump off *(if fitted)*, trimmer set to neutral, throttle friction nut loosened and unnecessary electrics and radios switched off.

Touch and Goes

In order to practise landings most efficiently, **"Touch and goes"** or **"rollers"** are performed. By this method you will be able to increase the number of circuits and thus the number of practice landings you can achieve in an hour, as compared with carrying out a full stop landing and having to taxy back to the holding point. In order to carry out the touch and go, during the landing run, flap is retracted to the take-off setting, full power is applied *(with carburettor heat having been set to cold)* and a normal take-off performed without having stopped.

If the runway you are using is fairly short, it may not be possible to achieve the touch and go, so if you are in doubt about having enough room to take off again, you should always stop and return to the holding point.

Balloons & Bounces

During training it is almost inevitable that some of the landings will be far from ideal. Several common faults will occur, usually as a result of over-controlling or misjudging the point at which to flare the aircraft. This judgment only comes with experience which takes time to develop. In some individuals it may take longer than others, but patience and perseverance will yield results.

Balloons

A balloon will occur when the nose is pitched up too quickly during the flare, or leaving too much power on at the point of flare, approaching at too fast an airspeed or even by a gust of wind. The correct technique to use in this situation is to go around immediately. This is essential for an inexperienced pilot, although as you gain experience it may be possible to correct from a balloon, especially a small one, by adding a little power and rounding out again. Failure to go around would result in the aircraft pitching up and then entering a quasi-stalled condition from which it would impact the runway very hard, possibly leading to damage.

Bounces

This can occur if there is a failure to flare and hold off correctly, or touching down too fast, perhaps with power still left on, also from flaring too high. A bounce can also occur if the nosewheel is allowed to contact the ground before the mainwheels. In all these cases you should immediately go around. It is very important to avoid a second bounce on the runway as this could develop into a series of ever increasing bigger bounces, eventually leading to the nosewheel hitting the ground with force. It is not unknown in that situation for the nosewheel to snap off!

The message in both these cases of mislanding and in all other situations which look or feel wrong:

Make an Early Decision to Go-around

The Go-Around

There are many reasons why it may be necessary to go around in addition to the mislanding cases described above.

- **Balloons or bounces**
- **Blocked runway – an aircraft, animals, vehicles or even stray people**
- **Too high or too low**
- **Too fast or too slow**
- **Not aligned with the runway centreline**
- **Unstable approach – either speed or direction**
- **Sudden windshear or turbulence**
- **Crosswind outside your experience**
- **A sudden shower reduces your visibility**
- **Too close to the aircraft in front**
- **An instruction from air traffic control to do so**

To initiate the go-around, make a firm and positive decision to do this. Then apply full power, being aware that from the approach configuration with low power, flap and trimmed for the descent, the pitch up when full power is applied, may be very strong. You will need to counteract this with forward pressure on the control column and rudder to balance. Initially fly the aircraft in a shallow pitch up and only once the descent has stopped retract flap to the take-off position. Then pitch up to adopt a climb, retracting the remaining flap when safely climbing away at an altitude of at least 200-300 feet. Trim for the climb. Once the manoeuvre is complete reintegrate into the circuit pattern. At a suitable point announce to air traffic control that you have **"gone around"**.

Do not be in a hurry to talk to air traffic control: remember:

Aviate - Navigate - Communicate

LESSON AIM

To learn safely and correctly the procedure for an abandoned approach to land.

LESSON OBJECTIVE

By the end of the lesson you will be able to demonstrate safely and correctly your ability to abandon a landing and to make a go-around.

AIRMANSHIP

Checks. RT. Climbing Out and Lookout.

AIR EXERCISE   *The Go-around and Missed Approach.*

Teaching Points

Go-Around

1) Sudden unexpected runway obstruction.
2) Too high-low to make a safe landing.
3) Balloon or bounced landing.
4) Mentally unprepared.
5) Good approach - poor alignment with runway in final stages.
6) Poor alignment with runway.
7) Unexpected cloud at lower level.
8) Poor visibility at lower level.
9) Unexpected turbulence.
10) Cross wind outside the aeroplane's limits.
11) Airspeed incorrect.

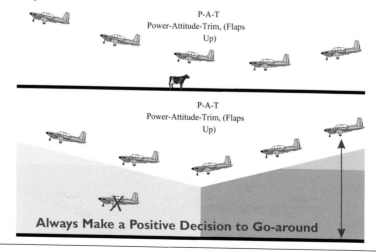

P-A-T
Power-Attitude-Trim, (Flaps Up)

P-A-T
Power-Attitude-Trim, (Flaps Up)

Always Make a Positive Decision to Go-around

Other Factors in the Landing

These factors are similar to the considerations we looked at when discussing the take-off: the effects of weight, altitude, temperature and wind.

Weight

If the aircraft is heavier than usual, it may be necessary to consider the effect on the length of the landing run. Added weight will also mean a higher touchdown speed i.e. 20% increase in weight = 10% increase in touchdown speed and as the faster aeroplane will take longer to slow down, a 20% increase in landing run.

Temperature and Altitude

Although the effect of altitude and temperature do not have as much impact on the landing run as on the take-off distance, they do become significant when operating at high density altitudes. *(Rarely experienced in the UK, but in South Africa, Europe and parts of the USA this factor is very important)*

Runway Slope and Gradient

As with the take-off, a surface such as long wet grass can increase the landing run by 30% or more. There will be poor braking action. A downsloping runway will also increase the ground run and additionally provide a distorted perspective of the approach angle. Looking at the diagram below, it can be seen that the approach to an upsloping runway will give the illusion of the pilot being too high, leading him to fly too low an approach in an attempt to correct for this. The reverse is also true.

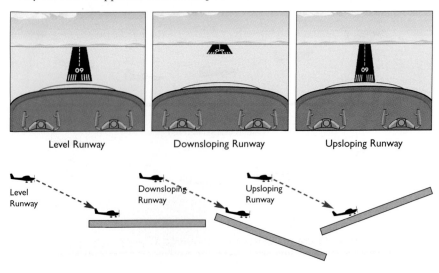

| Level Runway | Downsloping Runway | Upsloping Runway |

178

Wind

The effect of the wind on turning from base onto final has already been considered. On the final approach the effect of the wind is very significant. The main effect is to alter the ground speed and this is clearly important to the length of ground run. As with the take-off, landing into a headwind is desirable to reduce the approach speed. A 10kt headwind would reduce the ground run by approximately 20%, yet a 5 kt tailwind would increase it by 20%. Add a further factor of 1.43 *(43%)* for safety when calculating landing distance.

Wind near the ground can also give rise to turbulence, gusts and windshear. Due to surface friction and uneven heating of the earth's surface, turbulence near the ground is very common. Wind gusts or windshear occur where the wind direction suddenly changes. This can cause a sudden sinking of the aircraft and sudden fluctuations of airspeed, which reduces the aircraft's controllability. In these conditions it is advisable to increase the airspeed slightly or to make the approach flapless.

Wake Turbulence

This is a problem which can occur if you are operating at an airport where large aircraft operate. Wake turbulence is formed as vortices trailing back from the wingtips of aircraft particularly when taking off or landing. They are usually invisible and are most dangerous in light wind conditions when they do not disperse quickly. The vortices are sometimes so powerful as to turn a light aircraft upside down. The subject is dealt with in greater detail in Volume 4, but be alert for the potential problem if you are asked to line up and take off or follow on approach, a large jet transport aircraft or even a large helicopter.

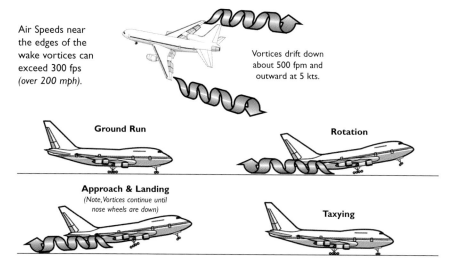

Air Speeds near the edges of the wake vortices can exceed 300 fps *(over 200 mph).*

Vortices drift down about 500 fpm and outward at 5 kts.

Ground Run

Rotation

Approach & Landing
(Note, Vortices continue until nose wheels are down)

Taxying

Departing and Joining the Circuit

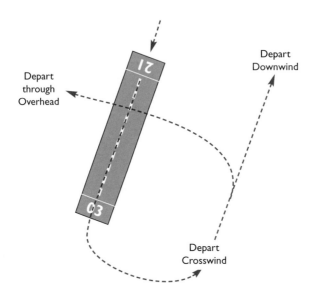

Some airfields will have non-standard procedures so you should always refer to the appropriate information about the circuit joining and departure as set out in guides such as Pooleys Flight Guide. It is important to follow any air traffic instructions and plan your departure so as not to conflict with other aircraft. It may be possible simply to leave the circuit by climbing out straight ahead, or from the crosswind or from the end of the downwind leg and then setting heading. Alternatively you may be permitted to climb up into the overhead to set course. You should set the QNH on the altimeter, so that it reads altitude above sea level.

Rejoining the circuit is likely to be subject to local procedures and you should set the QFE so that your altimeter reads height above the aerodrome, once you are visual with the field. Air traffic will give you instructions for the join which could be to join direct into the circuit either onto crosswind, downwind, base leg or even straight in on final approach. The alternative and most usual method in the UK is the Overhead join. You will overfly the airfield at 2000 feet and once cleared to do so descend on the **"dead side"** i.e. away from the active traffic pattern, down to circuit height. Then cross the upwind end of the runway to join the circuit pattern.

Teaching Points

Flapless Approach and Landing

1) A flatter flightpath (but not normally below 3° approach) requiring an extended circuit.

2) A higher approach speed due to higher stalling speed.

3) A higher nose attitude and poorer forward vision.

4) Reduced round-out and a longer float.

5) A risk of scraping the tail if the nose attitude is too high on touchdown.

6) A longer landing run.

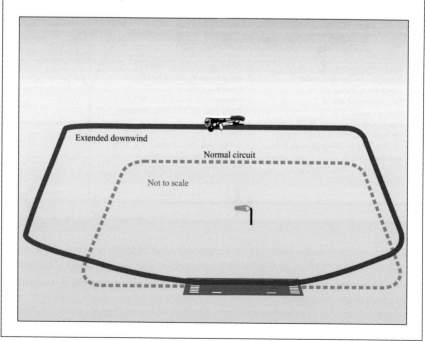

Normally the approach to land will be made with flaps to assist in controlling the aircraft better at a lower airspeed, and also to provide an improved forward visibility due to the lower nose attitude. If there is a mechanical or electrical failure of the flaps or the conditions are very gusty then the approach will be made without flaps.

The main considerations are seen on the diagram above. A flatter flightpath is used as a higher approach speed will be required. It is important to fly the correct glidepath for the runway, not getting too low, as there may be obstructions. Generally you will not fly below a 3° glidepath. The nose attitude will be higher which reduces your forward vision. The flare is much reduced but the float along the runway may be prolonged. Be careful not to scrape the tail if the nose attitude is held too high. The landing roll will be longer because of the faster approach and touchdown speed.

Glide Approach and Landing

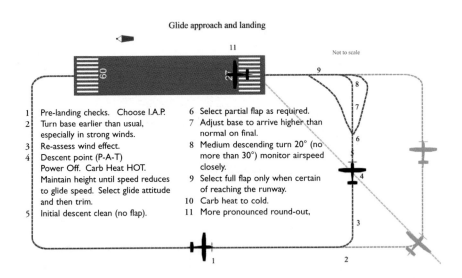

Glide approach and landing

Not to scale

1 Pre-landing checks. Choose I.A.P.
2 Turn base earlier than usual, especially in strong winds.
3 Re-assess wind effect.
4 Descent point (P-A-T) Power Off. Carb Heat HOT. Maintain height until speed reduces to glide speed. Select glide attitude and then trim.
5 Initial descent clean (no flap).

6 Select partial flap as required.
7 Adjust base to arrive higher than normal on final.
8 Medium descending turn 20° (no more than 30°) monitor airspeed closely.
9 Select full flap only when certain of reaching the runway.
10 Carb heat to cold.
11 More pronounced round-out,

NB: *Before closing throttle choose an initial aiming point (IAP) between ¹/₃ - ¹/₂ way into the runway - if the IAP appears to move up the canopy you are beginning to become too low (turn in) and vice versa. Flap should be used sensibly to bring the initial aiming point closer to the Threshold.*

The main reason for using this technique is to practise and gain judgment for use in the exercise of Practice Forced Landings *(Exercise 16)*. The approach path towards the runway will be controlled mainly by the use of flaps, although it is also important to judge the position of the aircraft on the base leg, manoeuvring as necessary.

When the approach is being flown without power, the approach path will be steeper, requiring the aircraft to be positioned higher than normal. The descent rate is greater and the nose attitude of the aircraft is lower, to maintain the approach airspeed. The lower nose attitude will require a more positive round out at the flare. If the roundout point appears to move up the windscreen or sidescreen you are becoming too low and vice versa.

Being aware of the effect of the wind will assist your judgment in where to close the throttle. Plan the circuit so that the base leg is shorter than usual and aim initially well into the field, approximately $^1/_3$ to $^1/_2$ way down the runway. Only select flap once you are certain of reaching the field and then only the last stage to bring your aiming point nearer to the end of the runway.

If you are too high on the approach, then widen out the base leg or make 'S' turns. Take flap a little sooner. If it looks as if you are becoming too low, then delay use of flap and cut in on base leg, aiming directly at the runway *(see diagram p182)*.

The round out will be more pronounced and the flare should be started slightly higher than normal. Do not try to stretch the glide, if the approach is badly judged it is better to go around and try again.

Crosswind Approach and Landing

Rule of Thumb	
30° difference between runway direction and wind direction:	Crosswind Component = ¹/₂ Windspeed.
45° difference between runway direction and wind direction:	Crosswind Component = ³/₄ Windspeed.
60° or more	all Crosswind

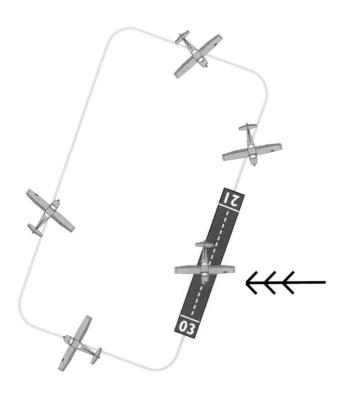

Using the crosswind table above you should calculate the crosswind component for the wind conditions on the day and ensure that not only do you not exceed the crosswind limits set for you by your flying school *(probably to be found in the Flying Orders Book)*, but also for the aircraft *(in the POH)*. During the circuit, the effect of the crosswind will have been noticed and due allowance for the drift should have been taken. Once you have turned onto base leg, the effect of a headwind will decrease your groundspeed and therefore you can delay commencing the descent. A tailwind will increase your groundspeed and there will be a tendency to get too high or to turn through the final approach path.

The main problem will be maintaining a straight track down the final approach. Two methods are commonly used to deal with the crosswind – the crabbed approach and the wing-down method. There is also the combined method which uses a bit of each! Since there are often gusts and turbulence associated with crosswinds, it is advisable to use less flap and a slightly higher approach speed to give better control. The flare is normal, but do not hold off too long, as the aircraft may drift sideways. During the landing roll use rudder to maintain a straight path along the runway, adding aileron progressively to keep the wings level. Lowering the nosewheel a little earlier and holding forward pressure on the control wheel will assist in directional control.

Crabbing

In this method, you should point the nose of the aircraft into wind and fly this offset heading to track down the approach path.

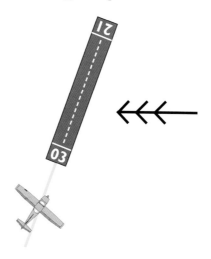

Just prior to touchdown use the rudder to align the longitudinal axis of the aircraft with the centreline. The key to success in this manoeuvre is timing, as too early application of rudder will lead to a sideways drift across the runway and the only solution is to prevent sideways drift with ailerons. Do not delay a decision to go around if the drift is too great. If you are too late with the rudder, then the aircraft will land sideways which will stress the undercarriage as it will tend to slew sideways across the runway. If the sideways tendency is recognised early it may be able to prevent the problem developing by applying a little wing down aileron to prevent lateral drift and using rudder to keep straight.

Wing Down

This method is a form of forward slip, ie the controls are crossed. To enter this, you should lower the into wind wing *(i.e. the aileron is raised)* and apply opposite rudder pressure to maintain a straight path aligned with the runway centreline. As you now have crossed controls, the balance ball will not be centred. Landing from the forward slip will mean that you will land on the into wind wheel and as the aircraft settles you should level the wings and the other mainwheel will touch down, and only then the nosewheel should be lowered.

Combining the two methods has some advantages. The wing down method is uncomfortable as the aircraft is out of balance. It is easier to land from this method however, so you could fly the crabbed approach as described above and then adopt the wing down method just prior to landing. Both methods take practice and with experience you will be able to judge the point at which to transfer from the crab to the wing down.

Short Field Landing

A short field landing is used where there is a confined space or, for example, part of the runway is unusable because of obstructions on the approach. Select the most into wind runway available in order to shorten the landing run with the headwind effect. On the final approach the aircraft should be flown at the lowest safe speed and full flap should be selected. The selection of full flap will permit a lower approach speed and less float on the hold off plus a shorter landing roll.

You will need to use more power to maintain the speed as you may be flying on the back of the drag curve.

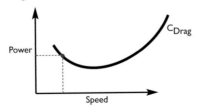

Try to cross the airfield boundary as low as possible after clearing any obstacles. Do not close the throttle too early as you may need to use the power to prevent too heavy a sink onto the runway as you flare the aircraft. The aircraft should touch down the moment the throttle is closed. If the runway is very short then use braking as appropriate in the landing roll. Be careful to ensure that all of the wheels are on the ground and then brake judiciously to avoid skidding, which may occur if too much brake is used too early.

Soft Field Landing

This technique should be used when landing at a grass airfield when you are not sure of the condition of the surface. It may also be required on sand, long grass or mud. The main problem is that the nosewheel may dig in and therefore a normal approach should be flown, but on the landing, the nosewheel should be held off and the touchdown made at the lowest possible speed. Keep a little power on in the flare to assist with control as you hold the higher nose attitude. Once you have landed try to avoid using the brakes unless absolutely necessary. More power to taxy may be required if the surface is very soft.

After Landing Checks

As part of good airmanship you should, in all cases, clear the runway and then **STOP**. Set the rpm to 1200 and then carry out the after landing checks from the checklist. Typically these will include checking that the carburettor heat has been set to cold, retracting the flaps, resetting the trim wheel, turning off unnecessary electrics and radios and the fuel pump, if fitted. You should obey air traffic instructions regarding taxying to park and keep the radio tuned until you reach a stop at the parking area. The shutdown checks should then be carried out from the checklist. See Chapter 2 for the after flight actions.

Left Intentionally Blank

Quiz No. 13

1. Normally a circuit pattern is ...... hand, at ...... feet.

2. Downwind, you should carry out ...... checks.

3. Between downwind and final approach is the ...... leg.

4. On final approach the call to air traffic control should be ......

5. After landing you should ...... of the runway and ...... before carrying out the after landing checks.

6. If your landing results in a bounce or "balloon" you should immediately make the decision to ......

7. Landing with a tailwind will ...... the landing roll.

8. During a flapless approach the flightpath will be ....

9. In a glide approach you should aim to land ...... the airfield, using ...... to bring the .... nearer the end of the runway.

10. Two techniques to use on a crosswind approach are .... or ....

Answers
No. 13

1.   Left, 1000.
2.   Pre-landing (BUMPFICH).
3.   Base.
4.   for Clearance to land or Touch and Go.
5.   Taxi Clear, Stop.
6.   Go-around.
7.   Increase.
8.   Flatter.
9.   Well into, Flaps, Aiming point.
10.   Crabbing, Wing Down.

Chapter 14 - Exercise 14

First Solo

14. LESSON AIM

To consolidate your training so far and to achieve the required standard for your first solo flight

LESSON OBJECTIVE

By the end of the lesson you will be able to demonstrate safely and correctly your ability to fly the aeroplane solo and complete a circuit by yourself.

AIRMANSHIP

Lookout. R/T. Aeroplane's performance improved. Emergencies. Relax.

Introduction

Before you are allowed to make your first solo flight you have to comply with a number of requirements:

- You must be at least 16 years old.
- You must have passed a minimum of a Class 2 medical examination with an authorised medical examiner (**AME**), unless you are seeking a NPPL when a certificate from your GP will suffice.
- It is recommended *(and usually your flying school will make it compulsory)* that you have passed the Air law ground examination and have sound technical knowledge of the aircraft.

The Flight

Only your instructor will know when you are ready to go solo. There is no minimum number of flights or flying hours before first solo, as everyone progresses at different rates. Before you achieve the standard required, you will have carried out a number of "**circuit sessions**" perfecting your landing technique and you will have practised various emergency procedures, including engine failure after take-off and the go around.

Your instructor will give you a briefing before sending you solo. Typically this will include the items set out below.

Exercise 14 — First Solo

LESSON AIM

To consolidate all your training so far and to achieve the required standard for your first solo flight.

LESSON OBJECTIVE

By the end of the lesson you will be able to demonstrate safely and correctly your ability to fly the aeroplane solo and complete a circuit(s) by yourself.

AIRMANSHIP

Checks. RT. Aeroplane's performance improved. Emergencies. Relax.

AIR EXERCISE — *First Solo.*

Teaching Points

Typical Instructor's Briefing

1) Carry out only one circuit.
2) If in any doubt about ATC instructions ask them to repeat it.
3) The aeroplane's performance will be improved ie. it will climb better without additional weight.
4) If you do not feel good about the approach or landing go around again.
5) I am confident in your ability.
6) When you have finished park and secure the aeroplane and I will see you back in the Op's room.

You should fly the circuit in exactly the manner you have been practising up till now, making the appropriate radio calls and positioning the aircraft correctly round the circuit. Although you may feel a little nervous or apprehensive, that is normal. Your instructor will not send you first solo unless he or she is totally confident of your ability. You may find that the aircraft climbs a lot better with only you on board.

Most people thoroughly enjoy their first solo. It is a significant milestone in a pilot's career as it is a never to be repeated experience. There is only ever one first solo!! You may feel a temporary sense of euphoria, but remember the first solo is only the beginning of the many solo flights you will have to make. It is the first major hurdle on the way to a licence and will probably act as a catalyst to spur you on.

Consolidation

After the first solo, you should not expect to fly again that day. The sense of euphoria needs to settle before you have your next lesson. Subsequent lessons will continue with circuit work as you will need to consolidate with more solo practice interspersed with periods of dual flying. Normally your instructor will accompany you for a few circuits, to ensure that you are not developing any bad habits and to assist you to refine your technique in differing wind conditions. Then you will carry out a few touch and goes on your own. Once you have gained a few hours of solo consolidation experience you will then move out of the circuit to practise departing the circuit and rejoining (see Chapter 12).

Intentionally left blank

Chapter 15 - Exercise 15

Advanced Turning or the Steep Turn

---

15. LESSON AIM

To learn safely and correctly the procedure for advanced turning ie. at steep angles of bank (45° or more).

LESSON OBJECTIVE

By the end of the lesson you will be able to demonstrate safely and correctly your ability to make a level turn of the aeroplane at 45° angle of bank or more.

AIRMANSHIP

Lookout. Loading factors in turning flight. Stalling airspeed v angle of bank.

Introduction

The object of advanced turning manoeuvres is two-fold: to improve your coordination and handling and to enable you to take evasive action if a collision is imminent. Remember from your study of the Rules of the Air *(Volume 2)* that if you need to take avoiding action you should normally make the turn to the right, so you will practise this too.

Forces in the Turn

We have already looked at the forces which affect the aircraft in turning flight, back in Chapter Nine. We have also considered the effect of increased '**g**' loading in Chapter Ten. During advanced turns you will be banking the aircraft to at least 45° of bank and up to a maximum of 60°.

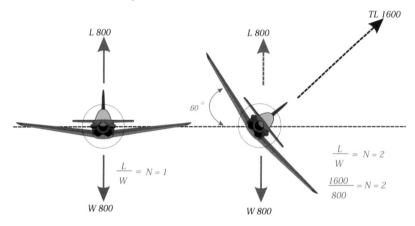

You will recall that in level flight the lift produced by the wings is balanced by the weight of the aircraft. In turning flight there is a horizontal component of lift called centripetal force which effectively pulls the aircraft into the turn. Increasing the bank angle will require an increase in lift to provide not only the vertical component *(as the lift is inclined)* but also the horizontal component. The extra lift required for a 60° turn is twice the weight of the aircraft. Increasing the angle of attack of the aircraft by increasing the backpressure on the control column will provide some of the extra lift required. The problem with this is that the increasing angle of attack will lead to a reduction in airspeed and the aircraft will be approaching its stall speed.

Load Factor

Normal load factor "N' or "g" is 1 when the aircraft is in straight and level flight or   stationary on the ground. This is experienced as your normal weight. As the bank angle is increased you will feel the increased '**g**' loading as if you were being pressed into the seat. At 60° of bank the effect is of double your weight *(see p196)*. As the load factor or '**g**' increases so does the stalling speed and this is a sign of an increased load on the structure of the aircraft.

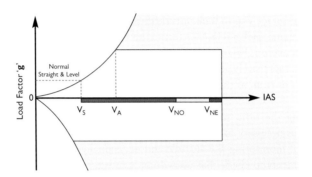

The limits of load factor of an aircraft will be set out in the POH. Aircraft are designed to withstand certain loads in flight, but the operation of the aircraft is subject to the strength limitations and overstressing the airframe could lead to serious damage. You have already come across certain of the '**V**' speeds. V_{NE} is the maximum speed at which it is safe to fly the aircraft and V_A is the maximum manoeuvring speed. This will usually be much lower than V_{NE}, as above the V_A speed, abrupt control deflections will cause an increased load on the structure.

Use of Power

The greater the angle of bank, the nearer the aircraft is to the stall. Addition of extra power in the turn will help to reduce the chance of stalling as the increase in thrust will assist with the production of extra lift and help to overcome the increase in drag, which has resulted from the increased angle of attack. It is necessary to add the power as the bank angle is increased and before the airspeed has reduced significantly. If this technique is not used, then the airspeed will reduce leading to a reduction in lift and a loss of altitude. Trying to regain the altitude by increasing the backpressure will simply lead to a further loss of airspeed and the aircraft will either descend or stall.

Basic Control Technique

Lookout is of extreme importance, as you will be turning at a greater rate than normal. Some flying schools will require you to carry out the **HASELL** check prior to commencing steep turns, as it is a semi-aerobatic manoeuvre. The effect of side by side seating will be more noticeable than with medium level turns. Sitting on the left hand side the horizon will appear to be much higher in the windscreen when you make a turn to the left, than when you make a turn to the right.

To encourage you to look outside during the manoeuvre, rather than looking at the instruments, pick a reference feature on the horizon. As you roll into the turn, banking with aileron, balance with rudder, and then add power as the aircraft rolls beyond 30°. Progressively add more backpressure on the control column to maintain altitude. Do not trim, as the turn is a transient manoeuvre.

During the turn, maintain a constant lookout and make small continual adjustments as necessary to maintain the turn and a constant altitude. Keep a work cycle going of monitoring the attitude and occasionally glancing inside the aircraft at the instruments to check that everything is satisfactory. (**L-A-I**) You should not allow the glance at the instruments to affect the quality of your lookout, which should remain vigilant. The main instruments to scan will be the altimeter and VSI to check constant altitude, the ASI to monitor airspeed, the AI to verify bank angle and the ball to ensure that you are in balance.

If you are gaining altitude reduce the backpressure and possibly increase the bank angle slightly. If you are losing altitude, reduce the bank angle, raise the nose with increased backpressure and then re-apply the bank.

Recovery to straight and level flight requires a little more anticipation of about 30° before the reference point or desired heading. In a coordinated fashion, you should roll the wings level with ailerons, releasing the back pressure and as the bank angle reaches 30° start to reduce the power to the cruise setting. If you forget to reduce the power then you will start to gain altitude once you have rolled level, or the airspeed will increase.

LESSON AIM

To learn safely and correctly the procedure for advanced turning ie., at steep angles of bank (45° or more).

LESSON OBJECTIVE

By the end of the lesson you will be able to demonstrate safely and correctly your ability to make a level turn of the aeroplane at 45° angle of bank or more.

AIRMANSHIP

Lookout. Loading Factors in Turning Flight. Stalling Airspeed versus Angle of Bank.

AIR EXERCISE   *Revise Medium Turns. Steep Turns.*

Teaching Points

Entry

1) Lookout.
2) Select a reference point.
3) Roll on bank with aileron.
4) Balance with rudder.
5) Apply sufficient back pressure on control column to maintain altitude.
6) Add power to maintain speed.

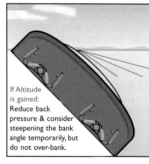

If Altitude is gained: Reduce back pressure & consider steepening the bank angle temporarily, but do not over-bank.

Maintaining the Steep Turn

1) Lookout.
2) Attitude: maintain bank with ailerons.
   maintain balance with rudder.
   maintain altitude with elevator,
   airspeed with power.
3) Instruments - check AI, altimeter, ball.

Recovery

1) Lookout.
2) Locate roll-out reference point anticipate by 30°.
3) Roll off bank with ailerons.
4) Balance with rudder.
5) Reduce power to maintain the required cruising airspeed.
6) Release elevator back pressure to maintain altitude.

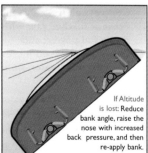

If Altitude is lost: Reduce bank angle, raise the nose with increased back pressure, and then re-apply bank.

Work Cycle: L - A - I

Correction of Faults-Unusual Attitudes

If the nose of the aircraft descends below the horizon in a steep turn, attempting to raise it by increasing backpressure will lead to a tightening of the turn, rather than raising the nose. This could rapidly lead to a spiral descent and as the airspeed increases, the danger of exceeding V_{NE} increases.

To recover from this condition:

- **Close the throttle**
- **Roll the wings level with aileron and rudder**
- **Ease out of the dive by applying back pressure on the control column; and**
- **As the nose pitches up above the horizon, check that the airspeed is reducing to the cruise speed and apply full power to regain altitude.**

The opposite to the low nose and high speed unusual attitude is the high nose and low speed combination. We have already seen the dangers with this in Chapters Ten and Eleven. Clearly there is the possibility of a stall even at a relatively high airspeed, because of the increased stall speed associated with the increased bank angle. If the aircraft has not yet stalled then the recovery action should be:

- **Apply full power and prevent yaw with rudder**
- **Roll the wings level**
- **Control column centrally forward**

If the aircraft does stall, then the recovery should be:

- **Control column centrally forward to unstall the wings**
- **Prevent further yaw with rudder; simultaneously**
- **Apply full power; and**
- **Once the airspeed increases roll the wings level with coordinated use of ailerons and rudder. Return the aircraft to level flight or a climb.**

One of the problems associated with stalling from a steep turn is the fact that you already have a high power setting or maybe even full power. The effect of a high power setting combined with the increased bank angle is to cause the stall entry to be much more violent, leading usually to a wing drop, which could be quite severe and if not promptly corrected an incipient or full spin could follow. If this occurs, then the standard spin recovery technique should be used *(see Chapter Eleven)*.

Steep Descending Turns

Teaching Points

Entry
1) From an established glide.
2) Look out.
3) Ailerons to roll aeroplane into bank.
4) Balance with rudder.
5) Lower nose to maintain descent speed (elevator).
6) Maintain good look out.

During the Steep Descending Turn
1) Lookout.
2) Maintain bank with ailerons.
3) Maintain balance with rudder.
4) Maintain SAFE airspeed with elevator.
5) Note the high rate of descent.

Recovery
1) Lookout.
2) Ailerons to roll wings level.
3) Balance with rudder.
4) Elevator, adjust attitude to regain glide speed.

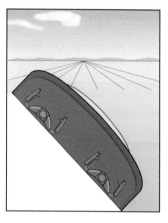

NB: For every 10° of bank beyond 30° add an extra 5 kts of airspeed to the best gliding speed.

Lookout - Attitude - Instruments

The steep descending turn may be made either from the glide or with power. In either case it is necessary to increase the airspeed in order to keep the airspeed sufficiently high above the stall. The purpose of the manoeuvre may be to descend through a small gap in the clouds or to effect a rapid descent for an emergency.

Enter the turn as usual but increase the airspeed with elevator. Beware as the nose will tend to drop in the turn and it may be necessary to hold a little backpressure once the turn has become established. If the turn starts to tighten up or the airspeed continues increasing, it is likely that you are entering a spiral descent, therefore recover as before. You will notice that the rate of descent will increase markedly as you increase the bank angle. Maintain the lookout especially below you, being aware of the blind spots.

Anticipate the rollout as the control forces will be quite coarse initially. Be especially careful of the altitude that you select for rolling out and ensure that you do not breach the low flying rules *(Rule 5)*.

Practice of these manoeuvres will improve your coordination and enhance your ability to handle the aircraft in unusual situations. You may find that you enjoy the experience of '**g**' in which case you may consider some aerobatic training after you have completed your PPL. Other people find the physiological effects of pulling a lot of '**g**' may lead to a little nausea. You will soon become accustomed to the effect of the pull down into your seat and if you clench your stomach muscles just prior to commencing the manoeuvre you will find that you can avoid the feeling. Your ability to tolerate '**g**' can be affected by hunger, fatigue, anxiety, level of fitness, alcohol consumption and whether you are a smoker.

Steep climbing turns are rarely practised in training aeroplanes as there is usually insufficient excess power to enable the aircraft to climb at an angle of bank greater than about 30 degrees. You can see this for yourself by entering a normal climbing turn at rate one and noting the reduced rate of climb as compared with the straight climb. Then increase the bank angle whilst maintaining the climb speed. Note how the rate of climb reduces. As you gradually increase the bank angle you will notice that the rate of climb will drop to zero, if you maintain best rate of climb speed.

Maximum Rate Level Turns

These turns are not usually practised on the PPL course, but they form part of the aerobatic syllabus for the AOPA Aerobatic Certificate. The maximum rate of turn that an aircraft can achieve is based on structural limitations and the power available. When the aircraft's bank angle has been increased to a point where it is no longer possible to maintain level flight, or the aircraft stalls, then it has reached its maximum rate of turn. From the graph on page 139, you will see that the stall speed increases dramatically as the bank angle increases and the '**g**' load factor increases. In training aeroplanes it is likely that the maximum rate of turn will be around 65 to 70° of bank. The only operational use for such a turn would be in order to effect an emergency collision avoidance manoeuvre. The result would be to turn the aircraft as quickly as possible through 90° and there would be no need to maintain accurate altitude in such circumstances.

As mentioned above, in the context of the work cycle, scanning the instruments will enable you to achieve more accurate turns. You can verify that the correct bank angle has been selected by glancing at the AI and check the VSI from time to time to achieve a constant altitude. Do not keep your eyes in the cockpit for more than a brief instant, as your lookout must not be allowed to degrade.

You may experience some buffet as your flying becomes more proficient. This is not the stall buffet, but your own slipstream or wake vortex. Do not worry about this - it is a sign of your improved accuracy!

Quiz No. 15

1.   In turning flight the horizontal component of lift called ...... pulls the aircraft into the turn.

2.   Increasing bank angle requires a corresponding increase in ......

3.   Adding power in a steep turn helps to reduce ......

4.   Mishandling the aircraft in the steep turn could lead to a ...... or an ......

5.   An important airmanship point in a steep turn is to maintain a constant ....

Answers
No. 15

1. Centripetal Force.
2. Power.
3. The risk of Stalling.
4. Spiral Dive, Approach to a Stall.
5. Lookout.

Chapter 16 - *Exercise 16*

Forced Landing without Power

Introduction

Main Causes of Engine Failure

Why would an engine fail? These days it is a very rare occurrence, although in the early days of flying there was greater unreliability. However, sometimes something may go wrong and it is important to have practised and become proficient at the emergency drills so that a safe landing can be made.

Fuel Starvation

This is the most likely cause of engine failure these days. It is also the most unnecessary cause. Mechanical problems are extremely rare, but unfortunately running out of fuel is still a regular feature in the incident and accident reports. So, carry out your pre-flight planning thoroughly. Not only should you calculate the fuel required for the flight, plus diversion and contingency margins *(consult your FTO for their desired method of calculation)*, but you should **VISUALLY** inspect the tanks. **DO NOT RELY** on the fuel gauges. They are often inaccurate. If you cannot see into the tanks, then use a calibrated dipstick appropriate to your aircraft. If in doubt refuel before departing. The only thing as useless as runway behind you and sky above you is fuel in the bowser… If you suspect fuel starvation in flight, depending on the aircraft type you may be able to switch on the fuel pump and change tanks. Careful monitoring of the fuel flow and consumption rate during the flight should avoid the problem developing.

Carburettor Ice

The next most likely cause of an engine stoppage in flight. Again, this is avoidable.

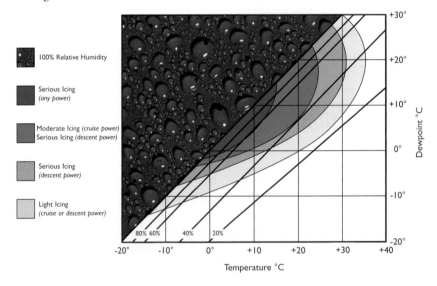

From the chart it is easy to see the most likely conditions conducive to formation of carburettor ice. In these conditions, you should be checking for ice even more regularly.

Mixture

If your mixture is incorrectly leaned for the altitude at which you are flying this may lead to an engine stoppage. If the primer has not been locked, it may have vibrated loose and the mixture could be over-rich leading to a "**rich-cut**".

Other less likely Occurrences

Can include a fire, a bird strike, mechanical breakdown within the engine, leading to loss of the engine oil, even a structural problem such as the propeller cracking or separating in flight. These are extremely rare events.

This exercise does not introduce any new *flying skills*; it is more about *planning* and use of resources.

I.   PRIORITY ACTIONS

These depend on altitude. If your engine stops or even suffers a partial loss of power, you, as the Captain of the aircraft have a prime responsibility - **TO FLY THE AEROPLANE !   DO NOT PANIC.**

• Immediately select carburettor heat to full hot

• Trim for the best glide speed for the aircraft - if you are flying a very fast aircraft it would be worth converting the excess speed to height by effecting a "**zoom**" climb, but this is not practical in our light training aeroplanes, where the margin between the cruise and the glide speeds is small. In chapter 13 we considered the glide approach and in most light single engine aeroplanes the gliding range will be approximately 9:1 enabling you to glide a distance of 9000 feet or 1.5 nm for every 1000 feet of altitude. How to assess gliding distance:

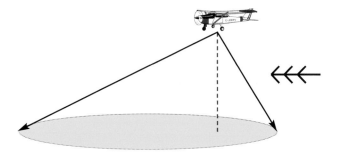

- Check the wind velocity and direction. You will have some idea of this from the time when you took off, as the air traffic controller should have informed you of the actual surface wind and you should be aware of the runway direction from which you departed. In addition, if there is any smoke drifting, this will help you to assess both the strength and direction.

- Select a suitable field: having decided the wind direction, naturally you will wish to orientate yourself to land into wind in order to reduce the landing speed and landing run *(see Chapter 13)*. It will be easiest for you in terms of flying the manoeuvre, if you pick a field out to the left, but in the real world you may not have any suitable fields out to that side. Do not forget that if there is someone sitting in the right hand seat they can assist you as they may be able to see a perfect landing area out on that side. A number of other factors will need to be considered for the selection of the field: **size, shape, surface, slope & surroundings.**

- **Size:** it is difficult to judge size from altitude, but you should select a large enough field, aiming to be able to land and stop safely within its boundaries.

- **Shape:** connected to the size is the shape - it is better to select a large squarish shape rather than a long thin field as it will give you more options for your approach and landing run.

- **Surface:** the best surface to select would be that which most closely resembles an airfield, but in the absence of an expanse of tarmac, short grass such as a pasture would be ideal. Avoid crops particularly if they look dark green or yellow as they will probably be tall standing crops and could cause an aircraft to nose over on landing. Similarly livestock can be a problem and a field with clumps of bushes or small trees is very unsuitable. It is difficult to see power lines from above and a really suitable-looking field may hold this hidden hazard which you only spot at a very low altitude when there are no other options. Avoid wet, marshy land as the aircraft will simply get bogged down and again may nose over. If you have to select a ploughed field then try to land along the furrows rather than across them.

- **Slope:** This aspect is very difficult to judge from above and if the field looks sloping it is probably a hill! Obviously it would be preferable if possible to land slightly uphill rather than down a slope.

- **Surroundings:** Note the undershoot and overshoot areas, also the position of your chosen field relative to others in case you need to make a late change of plan. It is not a good idea to make the approach over heavy woodland or other high obstructions as not only is this hazardous if you misjudge and undershoot the field, but also you may experience updrafts, which could severely destabilise the approach. If you have a choice, then it is a good idea to land near to civilisation, as you are more likely to be able to raise the alarm and obtain assistance if there is a road nearby or habitation of some sort.

2. PLAN THE DESCENT

How you plan your descent path towards the field is very dependent on your starting altitude. The higher you are the more options available to you. There are several ways to fly the manoeuvre, the most usual methods being the constant aspect method *(favoured by the military)* and the circuit pattern with 1000 foot area *(normally used in civilian training)*, or a combination of both.

NB: The 1000' area *(sometimes known as "low key")* should be selected at 45° and approximately 1 nm from the Initial Aiming Point. (**I.A.P**).

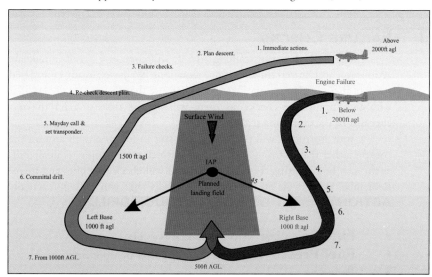

- Check your altimeter setting and be aware that you need to make adjustments depending on the altitude of the ground above sea level.

- Consider the wind velocity and direction.

- Choose a 1000 foot area. This should preferably be identifiable by a feature or obvious structure so that you do not lose sight of it as you track around the field. The idea is that you will arrive overhead the 1000 foot area at 1000 a.g.l. Thus if the ground is 400 feet above sea level at that point your altimeter would show 1400 feet.

- Plan your flight path towards the 1000 foot area. If you are well above 3000 feet it is best to circle around the field in a fairly tight pattern, to arrive at the upwind end at approximately 2500 feet. If you try to make a wider pattern around your field it will be more likely that you will either lose sight of it or you will misjudge the distance and be too far away from the field.

- Pick your initial aiming point (**IAP**) which should be at least $1/3$, preferably $1/2$ way into the field. It is better to reach the field and land a little far down it and collide with the hedge at the far end at, say, 20 knots, than to undershoot and impact the hedge in the undershoot, at 70 knots. If you do land a little long it may be possible to use braking to stop or to cause the aircraft to ground loop rather than having a collision.

3. FAILURE CHECKS

The POH for your training aircraft will contain a list of immediate actions to check in certain emergency situations. We have already considered some of these in chapter one. You should ensure that you are totally familiar with the appropriate checks, as there will not be time to refer to your checklist in the event of a real emergency.

Your instructor will probably teach you to follow a path around the cockpit rather than learning a set sequence which would apply to all aircraft, as this can be confusing. It is likely that you will check the following items. Remember when you are practising the drills that you will not actually **ACTION** these items, simply carry out **TOUCH DRILLS**.

- **Fuel Selector** - change tanks if possible
- **Fuel Pressure** - switch on the booster pump if fitted
- **Primer** - check it is in and locked

- **Mixture** - set to rich
- **Magnetos** - check on both
- **Carburettor Heat** - select hot and note response
- **Temperature & Pressure Gauges** - check readings for signs of anything abnormal - if there is no obvious sign of a cause for the engine failure, such as oil flooding out of the engine or a mechanical sign such as vibration, unusual noise etc, then try a restart. If the propeller is turning, then the action of switching the fuel and magnetos on should cause the ignition to activate.

4. Recheck the Descent Plan

If the engine does not start, then reconsider whether your plan to arrive at the 1000 foot area is working out. By now you will have had a chance to assess the effect of the wind and adjust the path as necessary.

5. MAYDAY CALL

Whilst you still have sufficient altitude to enable air traffic control to receive your transmission, it may be worth making an emergency call. This call should be made on the frequency you are currently using, or 121.5 MHZ. This should simply consist of sufficient details of the aircraft callsign, the location and the nature of the emergency. Keep the radio call brief and do not get involved in unnecessary conversation with air traffic control as there is little practical help they can give you at this stage. It will take the emergency services quite a while to reach you although they can be alerted, so an accurate position fix is of more use than the pilot's qualifications. The number of people on board is also useful information. Remember that it is more important to fly the aeroplane than to give a 100% accurate Mayday call: **AVIATE, NAVIGATE, COMMUNICATE.**

It can be helpful to set your transponder to 7700 as this may enable radar services to locate your position.

6. COMMITTAL DRILL OR SHUT-DOWN DRILL

Some people may describe these checks as the "**crash drill**" but this author believes that is too negative! The idea is to learn to land the aircraft safely thus consider that you are carrying out the procedures required in order to achieve that safe landing. Once you are committed to the landing and have decided that the engine will not restart it is best to carry out these drills as there will then be no indecisiveness *(wondering if the engine might start?)* and you can concentrate on the job in hand, i.e. landing safely.

- **Throttle** closed
- **Mixture** Idle cut-off
- **Fuel Off** and fuel pump off
- **Magnetos** off
- **Master Switch** off *(unless electric flaps fitted)*
- **Hatches** - unlatch to ensure that the door frame does not distort and prevent exiting from the aeroplane if the landing is hard or the aircraft rolls over.
- **Harnesses** - tighten as much as possible
- **Passengers** - brief them to adopt the brace position, using any available cushions or soft clothing to protect their heads. It is best if they remove any spectacles and dentures!

7.   FROM 1000 A.G.L.

As you approach the 1000 foot area, you need to concentrate on how you will plan the final stages of the approach. By now you will be able to see if there are any problems such as power cables, other obstructions or unsuitable surface, which would not have been visible from altitude. You can plan to adjust your approach path to land in the optimum direction. Adjust the base leg by widening it out if you are high or shortening the approach distance if you are getting low, because the wind is stronger than you estimated.

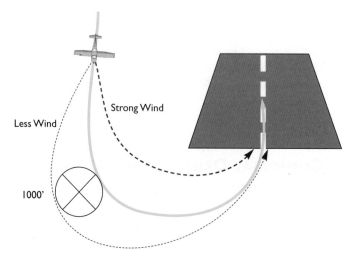

If you are still too high you can consider sideslipping *(if permitted for your aircraft type)* or making '**S**' turns. Only use flap once you are certain you will reach the field and use it in stages, adjusting the nose attitude and trimming between each stage to ensure that the airspeed remains constant. By using this technique you can start to adjust the roundout point from the IAP to bring the planned landing point closer to the near end of the field. Once you have turned onto the final approach, and you are quite sure of making it into the field, then select full flap. It is desirable to land at the slowest possible speed to ensure less damage and because you will not know what the surface is like until you land. Use the short field method, but also hold the nosewheel off as in the soft field technique as there may be unseen obstructions on the surface or ditches and holes.

8.   AFTER LANDING

Ensure that everything is switched off. Taking the fire extinguisher and the first aid kit, evacuate the aircraft and move yourself and the passengers upwind of it in case there is a fire or explosion. Protect the aeroplane and seek assistance. Telephone the police, try to locate the landowner and contact the flying school. If there has been a reportable accident, then you should also notify the AAIB *(see Volume 2 for more details)*. In this case the aircraft should not be moved until the AAIB investigators arrive or confirm that it may be moved. Under no circumstances should you attempt to take off!

Other Methods

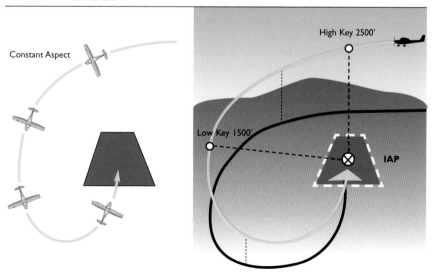

AIRMANSHIP

During the practice of this exercise, a number of important points must be considered:

- You will be simulating the engine failure, but you want to ensure that you do not end up in a 'real' emergency situation. Thus your instructor will simply close the throttle to simulate the emergency. You should of course immediately select and apply full carburettor heat if your instructor has not done this.

- As when you practised glide descents in exercise 8, you should warm the engine every 500 feet or so, to ensure that you will be able to achieve full power to climb away from the practice approach.

- When you have completed the approach you will execute a go around. Be sure to increase power to full power smoothly and not so rapidly that the engine backfires or simply cuts out due to rich-cut.

- Keep a vigilant lookout. Not only might there be other aircraft practising a similar exercise in the same area, but as you get lower, you run a greater risk of meeting other traffic such as helicopters, fast military jets or microlights. Power lines and high masts offer other dangers.

- Carry out all your checks carefully and methodically without hurrying but also without dawdling. You are practising for an emergency procedure and your drills should be meticulous and considered, not simply recited as a litany with no meaning. Be aware of the potential dangers which are associated with practising emergencies and understand which drills you should action and which should be 'touch' only.

- Do not breach rule 5 - remember that it is permissible to descend below 500 feet as long as you are not closer than 500 feet to any person, vehicle, vessel or structure. If you do decide to descend below 500 feet, however, be aware that when you execute the go around there will be a very strong pitch up tendency and a lot of forward control pressure will be required. If there are gusts or surface turbulence, you are not giving yourself much margin for error.

- When practising, do not use the same field for every practice. Be a good neighbour and move to a different field each time to avoid annoying people on the ground. Be aware, loud aircraft noise may cause livestock and horses to stampede.

Ditching in Water

If you have to ditch into water there are a few special considerations:

- Try to land near a ship if you are too far away from dry land. Remember that ships cannot simply brake and halt - it will take them a half mile or more to stop.
- Land along the swell. If you try to land into the waves you will probably nose over or suffer severe structural damage.
- Make a radio call as soon as possible whilst you still have the altitude to enable the call to be picked up. (**Use 121.5 MHz**)
- Brief your passengers; if they are not already wearing them *(which they should be from departure, in a single engine aircraft)* make sure they have donned their life jackets, but advise them not to inflate them in the aircraft. This would restrict their evacuation. Remove headsets and other objects which may restrict evacuation.
- Try to touch down at the lowest possible flying speed in a high nose attitude using a little flap and power to control the descent, if available, so that the tail impacts first. This will reduce the chance of nosing over.
- Inflate the life jackets once outside the cabin and if you have a dinghy, inflate it and as pilot in command you should supervise the passengers entering the dinghy.

In order to minimise the chances of having to ditch an aircraft, try to select the shortest route across water and fly as high as practically possible. This will increase the gliding distance available. You should always file a flight plan when flying across water outside the gliding range of land. Carry basic survival equipment and in winter consider wearing a survival suit. Over the northern latitudes during most seasons of the year, the average person would not survive more than about 30 minutes in the sea if not wearing a survival suit. Even in summer it is unlikely that this time would be increased much beyond a couple of hours. Always attempt to make land by at least one hour before sunset.

Left Intentionally Blank

Quiz No. 16

1. The most likely cause of an engine failure in a light aircraft is ......

2. The most important action in the event of an engine failure is to ...... the ......

3. The five 'S's are ......, ..., ..., ..., and ....

4. When practising forced landings, the failure checks are touch drills only, but should include: ......, ..., ..., ..., ..., ...

5. An emergency radio call should be made: this is known as a ...... call.

6. Once certain of reaching the chosen field, select .... and turn off the ......

Answers
No. 16

1. Fuel Starvation.
2. Fly, Aeroplane.
3. Size, Shape, Slope, Surface and Surroundings.
4. Fuel quantity, Selection of Tank, Carburettor Heat, Mixture Rich, Magnetos on both, Primer Locked.
5. Mayday.
6. Full Flap, Master Switch.

Chapter 17 - Exercise 17

Precautionary Landings

> ### 17. LESSON AIM
> To learn when and how to initiate a precautionary landing.

> ### LESSON OBJECTIVE
> By the end of the lesson you will be able to demonstrate safely and correctly your ability to initiate a successful precautionary landing.

> ### AIRMANSHIP
> Lookout. Location. Obstructions. Type of surface.
> Making a positive decision.

Introduction

Why would it be necessary to land other than at an Airfield?

There are a number of situations where a pilot has not exercised good airmanship for one reason or another or a problem which has arisen necessitates curtailing a flight before an alternative airfield can be reached. If doubt exists as to the wisdom of continuing the flight then it is advisable to make an early decision to land before conditions deteriorate still further and the landing becomes dangerous. What sort of reasons would necessitate this course of action?

- **Sudden deterioration in the weather**
- **Becoming totally lost**
- **Impending nightfall when unqualified for night flying**
- **Fuel state becoming critical**
- **Suspected aircraft problem**
- **Sudden incapacitation of the pilot e.g. food poisoning**

The first four of these reasons should all be avoidable with proper planning but unfortunately humans are fallible and tend to press on regardless hoping that things will improve. The likelihood is, that if one of the first four factors applies, then all the others will quickly follow, leading to a very serious situation. In these circumstances, a landing in an ordinary field rather than pressing on into worsening weather *(and perhaps having to fly on instruments in IMC when untrained, which nearly always leads to disaster)* is preferable.

Initial Procedure

•   If possible inform ATC or call on 121.5 MHz making a PAN call.

•   Check the wind direction and select a field using the same criteria as in exercise 16. There may be a disused airfield available, but be wary of these as they often have cracked or rough surfaces or fences and ditches placed along them which prevents usage.

•   Reassure your passengers.

•   Descend to position the aircraft downwind of the chosen field. Look for features to help you to locate the field, as at low level it is very easy to lose sight of a field due to the low level perspective - see also Chapter 18b.

•   Configure the aircraft to the slow safe cruise *(see exercise 6.2)* for a bad weather circuit. If the visibility is deteriorating this will assist you in a number of ways. The use of flap will improve your forward visibility due to the lower nose attitude; the slower speed and smaller turn radius will assist you in remaining near to your chosen field as you fly the circuit around it. Additionally the higher power setting gives you better elevator and rudder responsiveness *(better slipstream effect)*.

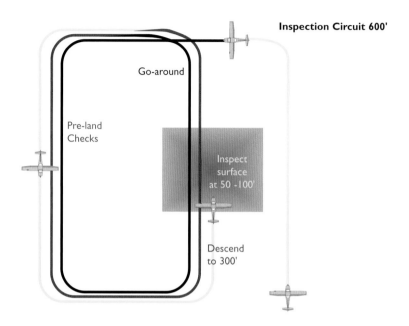

- The first inspection will be carried out at approximately 500-600 feet above ground level *(agl)*, particularly if there is a lowering cloudbase or bad weather. If there is simply reducing visibility, then the inspection can be done at 1000 feet agl. Note the direction of the intended landing path and calculate the reciprocal heading for the downwind leg. Note any prominent landmarks or features to assist in relocating the field. Check the surface for obstructions and slope.

- On the second inspection, descend on the base leg and fly an inspection run positioning slightly to the right of the intended landing area at approximately 200-300 feet. Look out for animals. Power lines and other obstructions. At the end of the landing area climb back up into the bad weather circuit.

- The final inspection run should be flown down to 50 to 100 feet so that a close inspection of the landing area can be made.

The Landing

Having completed the pre-landing checks, ensure that the harnesses are tight and then set the aircraft up for a short or soft field landing. Shut down and secure the aircraft after landing. Do not try to taxy it without first inspecting the surface visually for holes, ditches, wires etc. Only move the aircraft if it is necessary for its safety. Do not attempt to take off even if the weather clears, as landing away from a licensed aerodrome will have cancelled your authorisation to fly. Inform the flying school as soon as possible. You will also have to inform the landowner, the police and air traffic control.

AIRMANSHIP

There may be occasions when you will have to adopt the inspection procedure where landing at an unmanned field or farmer's strip. In these circumstances it is unlikely you will need to do more than one inspection circuit.

When practising the procedure, it is likely that your instructor will use your home-base airfield or take you to a suitable field, but if you have to practise in the local area you must be aware of not breaching any of the parts of rule 5. Do not annoy livestock or people. Keep a good lookout for other people using the same field for similar purposes.

ALWAYS make a positive decision to land. Do this when you have a state of Urgency not a state of Emergency. Do not leave making the decision until you have to land because you have run out of fuel or time or options.

Quiz No. 17

1. Reasons for landing other than at an airfield include: ......, ..., ...

2. If your reason for carrying out a precautionary landing is because of deteriorating visibility it is worth configuring the aircraft to the ....

3. Carry out an inspection circuit at ...... feet.

4. After landing ...... and ...... the aeroplane. Do no attempt to ......

Answers

No. 17

1. Deteriorating Weather, Impending Nightfall, Pilot Incapacitation (and others - see text).
2. Slow Safe Cruise.
3. 500 - 600.
4. Shutdown, Secure, Take-off.

Chapter 18 - *Exercise 18a*

Navigation

18. LESSON AIM

To learn to complete a cross country flight safely.

LESSON OBJECTIVE

By the end of the lesson, you will be able to demonstrate your ability to identify the basic requirements of flight planning to ensure safe navigation of an aeroplane on a cross country flight.

AIRMANSHIP

Checks. Lookout. Planning.

Introduction

After you have completed your basic flying training, you will then commence the navigation section of the course. The reason that you will complete the basic exercises first is to ensure that you have acquired sufficient handling skills to enable you to cope with the increased workload which will be experienced during navigation. The details of the navigation theory *(which you are required to pass the ground examination)* are set out in volume 3 of this series, but the practical aspects are summarised here.

Preparation

LESSON AIM

To Learn to complete a Cross Country Flight safely.

LESSON OBJECTIVE

By the end of the lesson you will be able to demonstrate your ability to identify the basic requirements of flight planning to ensure safe navigation of an aeroplane on a cross country flight.

AIRMANSHIP

Checks. Lookout. Planning.

AIR EXERCISE   *To Complete a Cross-Country Flight.*

Teaching Points

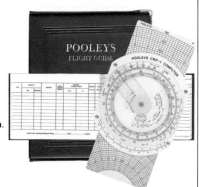

Personal Navigation Equipment

1) A good **Watch** that is clear and easy to read.
2) Up to date **Charts** for the route.
3) **CRP-I Computer**.
4) **Scales** (Ruler).
5) **Protractor**.
6) **Pens, Pencils, Lumocolor** or **Chinagraph**.
7) Up to date **Flight Guide**.
8) **Flight Log**, it should be accurate, easy to use and clear (often called a PLOG).

Good preparation is not only important to ensure that you navigate safely and accurately, but it is also a legal requirement. The pilot's responsibilities before flight are set out in the Air Navigation Order. Additionally, the more preparation you make before flight then the easier the flight will be!

• Satisfy yourself that the flight can be safely made taking into account the latest information available as to the route to be flown, airfields to be used and the weather conditions likely to be met en route.

• Prepare for alternative courses of action should the aeroplane become unserviceable or the weather deteriorate during the flight.

- Check that the aircraft is fit for the intended flight and all of the appropriate documents are in force.

- The aircraft should be operated within the maximum all-up weight and the C of G should be within the permitted range.

- Check that sufficient fuel and oil is loaded and there is a safe margin for contingencies and diversions.

- The departure and destination and any diversion aerodromes are suitable in terms of runway length for safely taking off and landing.

Route Selection

It is usual in most FTOs in the UK to use the 1:500,000 aeronautical charts for navigation. Having checked that your navigation chart is up to date *(they are republished regularly)*, start by reviewing the options. Can you simply draw a straight line from your aerodrome of departure to your destination? It is likely that there will be reasons why you cannot do this, such as obstructions, controlled airspace, high ground, prohibited, restricted or danger areas, MATZs and other active airfields.

Weather

Before you start the planning, obtain all of the required weather, the most up to date available, actual reports and forecasts (**METARS** & **TAFS**) for the planned route and destination airfields, plus any diversion airfields. Weather information is available from a number of sources *(see volume 2, part 2 Meteorology for more details):*

- **Briefing rooms at airfields where you will find print outs of the Area Forecasts and some TAFs and METARs.**
- **By telephone from the Met office automated AIRMET service**
- **By fax from the dial-up MET-fax service**
- **From the internet – there are a number of commercial providers as well as the MET Office's own site**

All of these sources are listed in a handy pocket size publication called GET MET, which is available free of charge from the MET Office or the CAA.

You need to establish that, as far as can be deduced from the available information, your flight can be safely completed whilst maintaining VMC. Of course weather forecasts are just that, a forecast, – they can never guarantee that the forecast conditions will arise. That is why contingency and diversion planning needs to be built in to your preparations.

Flight Log

Details of how to complete the flight log are set out in Volume 3 of this series. Always ensure that the flight log is completed legibly and that you double check your calculations for headings etc. It is easy to transpose figures and make gross errors which will lead to total confusion once you are airborne!

<table>
<tr><td colspan="2">POOLEYS</td><td colspan="12" align="right">VFR FLIGHT LOG</td></tr>
<tr><td colspan="4">PILOT D. GILL</td><td colspan="4">AIRCRAFT G- DOTS</td><td colspan="6">DATE 01-04-03</td></tr>
<tr><td colspan="4">FROM SHOREHAM</td><td colspan="2">TO STAPLEFORD</td><td colspan="3">DIST 66 n.m</td><td colspan="5">ETD/ATD 10.00 Z</td></tr>
<tr><td colspan="4">USEABLE FUEL</td><td colspan="3">GPH</td><td colspan="3">TOTAL REQ</td><td colspan="4">RESERVE</td></tr>
<tr><td>FROM /TO</td><td>SAFE ALT</td><td>PLAN ALT</td><td>TAS</td><td>TR (T)</td><td>W/V</td><td>HDG (T)</td><td>HDG (M)</td><td>G/S</td><td>DIST</td><td>TIME</td><td>ETA</td><td>ATA</td></tr>
<tr><td>SHOREHAM
BEHL WATER</td><td>2·2</td><td>2·4</td><td>90</td><td>063</td><td>190/20</td><td>073</td><td>076</td><td>100</td><td>30</td><td>18</td><td></td><td></td></tr>
<tr><td>BEHL WATER
STAPLEFORD</td><td>2·4</td><td>2·4</td><td>90</td><td>345</td><td>190/20</td><td>340</td><td>343</td><td>118</td><td>36</td><td>18·3</td><td></td><td></td></tr>
<tr><td></td><td></td><td></td><td></td><td></td><td>/</td><td></td><td></td><td></td><td></td><td></td><td></td><td></td></tr>
<tr><td></td><td></td><td></td><td></td><td></td><td>/</td><td></td><td></td><td></td><td></td><td></td><td></td><td></td></tr>
<tr><td></td><td></td><td></td><td></td><td></td><td>/</td><td></td><td></td><td></td><td></td><td></td><td></td><td></td></tr>
<tr><td></td><td></td><td></td><td></td><td></td><td>/</td><td></td><td></td><td></td><td></td><td></td><td></td><td></td></tr>
<tr><td colspan="3">START UP</td><td colspan="3">TAKE-OFF</td><td colspan="3">LANDED</td><td colspan="4">SHUT-DOWN</td></tr>
<tr><td colspan="13">CLEARANCES/OBSERVATIONS</td></tr>
<tr><td colspan="13"></td></tr>
<tr><td colspan="13"></td></tr>
<tr><td colspan="13"></td></tr>
<tr><td colspan="13"></td></tr>
<tr><td colspan="13"></td></tr>
<tr><td colspan="13"></td></tr>
<tr><td colspan="13"></td></tr>
<tr><td colspan="3">COMMS & RADIO NAV INFO</td><td colspan="10">DIST 121.50•TRANSPONDER DIST 7700•COM FAIL 7600•CONSPICUITY 7000</td></tr>
<tr><td colspan="2">STATION</td><td>SHM</td><td colspan="2">LND</td><td colspan="2">STAP.</td><td></td><td></td><td></td><td></td><td></td></tr>
<tr><td colspan="2">FACILITY</td><td>APP</td><td colspan="2">INFO</td><td colspan="2">A/G</td><td></td><td></td><td></td><td></td><td></td></tr>
<tr><td colspan="2">FREQ.</td><td>123.15</td><td colspan="2">124.6</td><td colspan="2">122.8</td><td></td><td></td><td></td><td></td><td></td></tr>
<tr><td colspan="13">Pooleys Flight Equipment Ltd • Tel: 020 8953 4870 • www.pooleys.com</td></tr>
</table>

Notams & Temporary Navigation Warnings & Bulletins

You should always check the latest NOTAMs and AICs for up to date information which may be relevant to your route and the destination and alternate, particularly in the summer, there are a large number of airshows and displays which may be arranged at fairly short notice. Also other operational information may change due to work in progress at an airfield. This information is much easier to obtain these days since much of it is available on the internet. In addition your flying club or school will post the information on the notice board together with the latest weather information.

Safety Altitudes and Cruising Altitudes

You should calculate a suitable altitude for each leg of the flight. Usually this will be at least 1000 feet above the highest obstacle within 5 or 10 nautical miles either side of your track. *(Your instructor will guide you on his preferred method)* Your safety altitude can also be calculated by adding 1000 feet to the MEF *(maximum elevation figure)* shown on the chart. The figure shown will be the highest obstacle within the rectangle bounded by each line of latitude and longitude, or if there is high ground shown, then a notional 299 feet will have been added to the highest spot height shown to represent an unmarked obstacle, then the figure is rounded up to the nearest 100 feet. *(Remember, only obstructions higher than 300 feet have to be shown on the chart)*. Thus you may see a MEF of 1_2 shown *(i.e.1200 feet)* but only find a spot height marked of 834 feet.

Bearing in mind the low flying rule *(rule 5)* calculate the minimum safe altitude at which you could fly if cloud forced you to descend. You now have a safe **"layer"** in which you can fly. Never fly below the minimum safety altitude – if you have to descend this low then you should be turning around and going back. In spite of this basic point there are still a number of accidents every year where pilots fly into high ground (**CFIT** – *Controlled Flight Into Terrain*). This is a totally avoidable accident which simply requires the correct decision to be made, early enough. Unfortunately too many people suffer from "press-on-it-is", which usually leads to disaster.

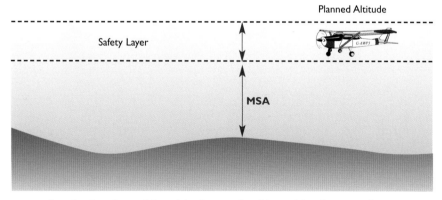

In selecting the cruising altitude you should consider the type of terrain over which you are flying, any airspace restrictions and the strength of the wind. If possible, fly as high as you can as you may be able to benefit from a strong tailwind and also lean the mixture more effectively for better fuel economy.

Fuel Plan

Your flying school may have its own rules about how you should calculate your fuel required for a cross country flight. This may be set out in the Flying Orders Book. Check whether the consumption figures used are taken from the POH and bear in mind that those figures will have been calculated to sell new aeroplanes. It is likely that the aeroplane that you are flying is far from new and the actual fuel consumption figure may be far higher.

Always ensure that you carry enough fuel for a diversion, plus a margin of at least 45 minutes fuel to be remaining in the tanks at the end of the flight. You should also add a contingency of 10% of the total to allow for unexpected contingencies or not having correctly leaned the fuel.

Weight and Balance (Mass & Balance)

Once you have calculated your fuel requirement, decided on your passengers and baggage you can then calculate the weight and balance and centre of gravity *(C of G)* position. This is very important for the reasons we have discussed in earlier chapters, i.e. the aircraft handling will be affected if the C of G is too far aft or too far forward and if the maximum certified weight for the aircraft is exceeded it can cause structural damage. This will also invalidate the Certificate of Airworthiness of the aircraft.

If your calculation shows that the weight is too great you will have to leave out a passenger or some baggage or load less fuel. If the latter, it will then be necessary to plan a suitable stop en route to uplift more fuel.

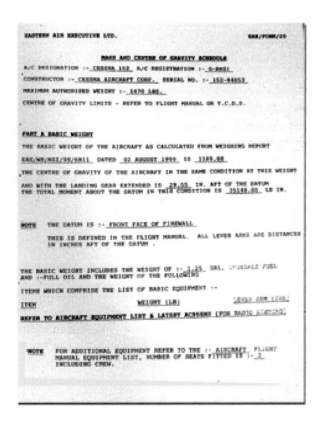

Take-off and Landing Performance

Once you have calculated your weight and balance and checked the weather at the destination airfield you should ensure that the required distance for the take-off and landing at the departure and destination airfields and any diversion airfields will be adequate. You will find the appropriate data for your aircraft in the POH. The official source of data for the airfields is in the AIP *(Aeronautical Information Publication)*. This document is regularly updated and you may find now that your FTO has the information on a CD for use on the computer. There are also a number of commercial publications which are convenient to carry with you on the flight, such as Pooleys Flight Guide, but these are not updated as regularly.

Alternate Airfields

An alternate airfield should always be included in your planning as many reasons may arise during the flight such as unforeseen bad weather, the runway becoming blocked or aircraft unserviceability. Ensure that the chosen alternate airfield is adequate in terms of runway length and direction as regards the wind direction and forecast windspeed. Make sure that you have noted the radio frequency and any other necessary information.

Radio Frequencies

Although the radio frequencies are printed on the side of your aeronautical chart, remember that the chart is only published once a year and there are sometimes changes. Therefore you should also check the AIP and Notams for these. Note all of the required frequencies on your flight log. It is worth noting that military facilities are often closed completely at weekends.

Booking out or Flight Notification

Normally you will have to complete formalities such as signing the technical log and perhaps an authorisation sheet. At some airfields you may need to telephone your details to air traffic control, although many simply require "**booking out**" over the radio. In this case you will give details of the aircraft type, registration, intended destination and number of passengers.

It may be necessary to file a flight plan for certain types of flight *(see volume 2 Air Law for details)* and if so you will need to do this at least one hour before intended start-up. A flight plan form may be filed by telephone or fax or even direct through a computer link. Details will be found in the flight briefing room at your airfield.

The Flight

Cockpit organisation; Start up and taxy

Before starting the engine, ensure that you can easily reach all of the charts and other equipment you may need during the flight. It is not helpful to realise part way to your destination that the radio frequency you require is in the flight guide in your flight bag at the rear of the aircraft. Make sure that the chart is folded in such a way you can easily follow the track, if possible orientating the chart so that the trackline goes up the chart. Ensure that you have highlighted your required headings in a bright colour so that you do not confuse them with any of the other calculations on your flight log. It is a good idea to have a spare pen or pencil to hand as sod's law always operates when you only have one - you either drop it or it breaks! Brief your passengers on the use of the seatbelts and evacuation procedures as well as emergency equipment. Follow your normal start up procedures, request taxy instructions and ensure that the power checks and pre-takeoff checks are completed.

POOLEYS   **VFR FLIGHT LOG**

PILOT **D. GILL**   AIRCRAFT **G - DOTS**   DATE **01-04-03**

FROM **SHOREHAM** TO **STAPLEFORD** DIST **66 n.m** ETD/ATD **10.00 Z**

USEABLE FUEL   GPH   TOTAL REQ   RESERVE

FROM /TO	SAFE ALT	PLAN ALT	TAS	TR (T)	W/V	HDG (T)	HDG (M)	G/S	DIST	TIME	ETA	ATA
SHOREHAM BEAL WATER	2·2	2·4	90	063	190/20	073	076	100	30	18		
BEAL WATER STAPLEFORD	2·4	2·4	90	395	190/20	340	343	118	36	18·3		

START UP   TAKE-OFF   LANDED   SHUT-DOWN

CLEARANCES/OBSERVATIONS

COMMS & RADIO NAV INFO   DIST 121.50•TRANSPONDER DIST 7700•COM FAIL 7600•CONSPICUITY 7000

STATION	SHM	LOND	STAP.		
FACILITY	APP	INFO	A/G		
FREQ.	123.15	124.6	122.8		

Pooleys Flight Equipment Ltd • Tel: 020 8953 4870 • www.pooleys.com

Take Off and Set Heading

Before applying the power and after ensuring that the aircraft is correctly lined up, check that the DI and the magnetic compass are aligned and reading correctly for the runway direction. The easiest method of departing from the airfield for a cross country flight is to climb up into the overhead and once at the planned altitude, set heading and start timing the first leg of the route. Unfortunately this is not always possible due to airspace restraints or local regulations. You may therefore have to plan the departure from a known feature near to the aerodrome, perhaps a VRP. Alternatively you may depart from the downwind position in the circuit and then you can start the timing from abeam the airfield. Since you are likely to know the local procedures at the planning stage, it will make sense to build this into the planning and draw the track line from the start point rather than from directly over-head the airfield.

Once you have reached your cruising altitude, carry out a cruise check (**FREDA**). Make sure that you have set the airfield QNH on the altimeter. Once you change radio frequency to the next service, you will request the regional QNH unless it has already been given to you on departure. Within a few minutes, it is sensible to check for gross error by positively identifying a ground feature. This will confirm that you have selected the correct heading and are in fact on track. It is not unknown for a pilot to be so overloaded with tasks at this stage of his flight that he scrambles the heading and flies 210° instead of 120°!

En route Navigation

You will already be familiar with the area around your home airfield but as you start to fly further away the features will become unfamiliar. You may find therefore that you are spending a lot more time looking at the chart trying to identify the features. It is easy to become over absorbed in this to the detriment of your lookout. It is also important to maintain a constant heading and altitude *(remember straight and level flight??)*. A log needs to be kept of the times you pass each selected waypoint together with estimates for the ones to come. Set the watch - put the map away and look ahead at a fixed feature. Wait for the time period to elapse.

AVIATE - NAVIGATE - COMMUNICATE

Your waypoints should have been selected during the planning stage, the first to be about 10 minutes flying time after departure to ensure that you are on track.

If you arrive overhead your first waypoint within a minute or so of your estimated time, then you can be fairly sure that the wind is as forecast and that you are holding a steady heading. If you are not on your track it will be necessary to use a method to regain track. Your trackline should have been divided into $1/4$, $1/2$ and $3/4$ sections and it may also be helpful to add a drift line *(5° or 10° your instructor will advise his preferred method)*.

Regaining Track

Normally it is preferable to use some simple method *(a rule of thumb)* rather than attempt to use calculators or complex mental arithmetic whilst flying the aeroplane. Whilst your instructor will advise his preferred method, you should be aware of the options:

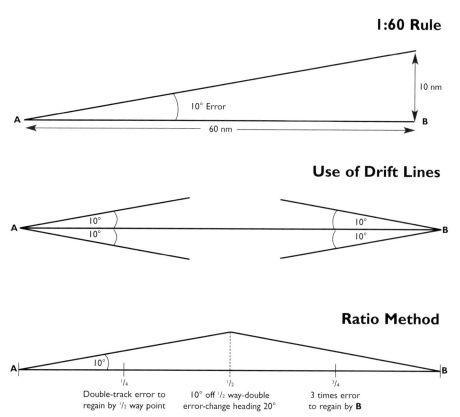

1:60 Rule

A — 10° Error — B
10 nm
60 nm

Use of Drift Lines

A — 10° 10° — 10° 10° — B

Ratio Method

A — 10° — $1/4$ — $1/2$ — $3/4$ — B

Double-track error to regain by $1/2$ way point

10° off $1/2$ way-double error-change heading 20°

3 times error to regain by **B**

Make sure that you note all the times at turning points and waypoints, together with any calculated revisions to track on your flight log. Some instructors advise that you mark the times on your chart in large figures although this can sometimes be a distraction as it may lead to important features being concealed.

Carry out regular cruise checks using the mnemonic, FREDA and ensure that you realign the DI and magnetic compass if required. Failure to do this is one of the most common causes of students becoming lost.

Use the radio to assist you on your flight. You can obtain valuable information about possible conflicting traffic and deteriorating weather in good time to take avoiding action. Do not be afraid to ask for assistance and to obtain a flight information service or radar information service if it is available. The assistance of radar in informing you of traffic relieves a little of the workload as it directs your lookout.

Arrival at Destination

When you are within about 10 to 15 minutes of your estimated arrival time you should request a frequency change to the destination air traffic service. If available, obtain the ATIS *(aerodrome terminal information service)* or request airfield data from the approach or tower service. Naturally you will have already planned your arrival and worked out how you are going to effect the join at the destination airfield, for the appropriate runway, but if the wind direction has changed *(not uncommon at coastal airfields which suffer from sea breeze effect!)* some hurried replanning may be necessary. It is likely that you will be required to carry out the overhead join at 2000 feet, letting down on the deadside to join the circuit pattern. You may be asked to join downwind or even direct onto base leg. Follow the air traffic controller's instructions. After landing you will be given directions to the parking area and then, having carried out your shut-down procedures, you should book in. There is usually a large sign with a big '**C**' in a square to denote where you book in. Pay your landing fees and refuel if necessary.

Sometimes the weather forecast will not be accurate and the actual weather en route deteriorates beyond an acceptable minimum for you to continue to your destination. In this case it will be necessary to carry out an in-flight diversion. What sort of conditions will require you to divert? You have learnt in air law about the Visual Flight Rules (**VFR**) and also about visual meteorological conditions (**VMC**). This is where the practical application of the rules will be required. Whilst you are aware that legally a PPL may fly in uncontrolled airspace with an inflight visibility of 3 km if below 3000 feet and at an airspeed of less than 140 knots, in practical terms it is extremely difficult to navigate in such low visibility. Similarly you will have calculated your minimum safe altitude for the route. If you have to descend this low, then you should really be turning back.

One of the problems which will occur in this situation is the sense of pressure from your passengers who want to get home, or from yourself, as you may experience a sense of failure if you have to turn back or divert. Forget this! As the pilot in command you have responsibility for the safety of your passengers and the aircraft and these should never be jeopardised by any misplaced sense of pride. You will never be criticised for turning back, but pressing on into deteriorating weather conditions which may cause you to fly into cloud or otherwise break the regulations is **DANGEROUS** and **ILLEGAL**. If you survive *(and many do not)* you will be in danger of prosecution or worse.

Therefore follow these rules on diversions:

Exercise 18a Navigation, Part 3 of 3

Teaching Points

Diversion to Alternate Airfield

1) Be positive about the diversion. Flying into deteriorating weather **MAY** kill you.
   A passenger may need medical attention or feel ill, it's your responsibility.
2) Inform ATC. Aviate - Navigate - Communicate.
3) Mark the new track on the map and estimate the new heading and distance.
4) Turn onto the new heading and record the time.
5) Positively identify a ground feature to ensure the heading is correct.
6) Map read accurately and check the ground features.
   Counter for any drift and calculate ETA and fuel.
7) Correct Track and Time errors at the halfway point if possible.

To assist you in planning the diversion, it can be helpful to carry a pencil which has been marked to show 10 mile sections *(i.e. 6 minutes if you are flying at 100 knots)*. You want to minimise the amount of time that you are looking down at your map and kneeboard and trying to calculate headings, distance and time to the new destination since your lookout will be degraded. Your instructor will brief you on his preferred method. See Volume 3 for further details.

Uncertain of Position

This is not the same as being lost. It should be possible to work out a dead reckoning position which can then be backed up with a positive fix over a known ground feature.

Uncertain of your Position

1) Log your compass heading, DI heading and time.
2) Check your DI against the compass.
3) Check you are steering the heading in your flight log.
4) Calculate the approximate distance travelled since last known ground feature.
5) Identify a major landmark.
6) Inform ATC.
7) Ask for help without hesitation.

If you are unable to ascertain your position after these procedures, then you should follow the "**Lost Procedure**" set out below.

Lost Procedure

Procedure when Lost

1) Don't fly around aimlessly, it will waste fuel and valuable time and you will become disorientated.

Fly the Aircraft

2) Stay calm, and remember your training, the situation will only get worse if you panic.
3) Maintain your heading.
4) Check DI, compass and flight log.
5) Check the fuel remaining and sunset time.
6) Is the compass being affected by an object placed near it?
7) Consider requesting a QDM, QTE or Radar Steer *(see chapter 18c)*.
8) Start checking from last known position regarding heading and time.
9) Read the map from ground to map, is there a unique feature?
10) **Check the safety altitude and the proximity of any controlled airspace.**
11) Estimate the distance flown from your last known position and apply it to the track plus or minus 10% then draw 30° drift lines either side of your track. This should denote the area you are in.
12) Inform ATC and ask for help, or make a PAN call on 121.5.
13) Follow the necessary instructions from ATC or from the distress and diversion call.
14) In the worst event carry out a precautionary landing.

Why did you become Lost?

- You may have made an incorrect calculation of heading, groundspeed or time estimate at a waypoint.

- As mentioned earlier, the most common reason is misaligning the DI so that you do not fly the correct heading.

- Incorrectly applying magnetic variation or drift can lead to problems *(double-check your calculations before departure and think through the 'gross error check')*.

- Misidentifying a ground feature as a waypoint *(look for at least three unique features to confirm that the feature is in fact your chosen waypoint)*.

- Deteriorating weather reduces visibility and increases your workload in the cockpit, thereby leading to a greater chance of mistakes.

- Failing to carry out regular cruise checks so that a slight error becomes magnified.

Quiz No. 18a

1. The usual aeronautical chart for navigation has a scale of 1: ......

2. When planning your altitude to fly, add at least ...... feet to the highest obstacle within 5-10 nautical miles of your track.

3. When calculating how much fuel you should take for a cross-country flight, allow a margin of ...... remaining at the end of the flight.

4. You should plan for an alternate airfield for ...... such as ......, ... or ......

5. Several methods of remaining on track during a flight exist: ......, ... & ....

6. If you have to divert to another airfield, then make a ...... decision early.

7. If you become lost then you could request ...... or ...... from air traffic.

Answers
No. 18a

1. 500,000.
2. 1000.
3. 45 minutes.
4. Contingencies, unforeseen Bad Weather, Runway becoming blocked, Aircraft Unserviceability.
5. I in 60 Rule, Use of drift lines, Ratio Method.
6. Positive.
7. A QDM, Radar Steer.

Chapter 18 - Exercise *18b*

Navigation at Lower Levels and in Reduced Visibility

18b. LESSON AIM

To learn how to navigate safely at lower levels and in poor visibility.

LESSON OBJECTIVE

By the end of the lesson you will be able to demonstrate your ability to navigate safely at lower levels and your understanding of the procedures to use when the visibility has reduced and/or the cloud base is lowering.

AIRMANSHIP

Lookout. Location. Weather. Safe altitudes. High ground and obstacles. Effect of drift and groundspeed.

Introduction

Low level flying may be required in several different circumstances but at all times you should be aware of your responsibilities as a pilot and the need to comply with the ANO and the Rules of the Air. In practice you should not breach any part of rule 5 i.e. you should not fly within 500 feet of any person, vessel, vehicle or structure except when taking off or landing. In addition, your flight over a built-up *(congested)* area should not be below 1500 feet of the highest structure within 600 metres of the aircraft or such height as would enable you to glide and alight clear of the area in the event of an engine failure. If there is a large open-air gathering *(e.g. a football match)* you should not fly within 1000 metres of it nor below 1000 metres. In practising low level navigation, therefore, it will be necessary to fly round most settlements.

Generally low level is considered to be below 1500 feet and down to about 500 feet, although the military will fly lower than this *(they have special exemptions from the civil rules)*.

Reasons for low level flying include:

- **Deteriorating weather conditions**
- **Inspection of a field prior to executing a precautionary landing**
  (see *Chapter seventeen*)
- **Planned entry into the VFR Entry and Exit lanes which provide access to certain airfields beneath controlled airspace. This may be necessary to ensure a safe separation from IFR** (*Instrument Flight Rules*)
  traffic above.

Low Level Familiarisation

A number of factors will become apparent when operating at low level. These will include the increased workload due to the fact that the ground features will be more difficult to interpret, making map reading more difficult, there will be more likelihood of turbulence rendering handling the aircraft more challenging and if the exercise is being carried out in real conditions, then the poorer visibility and lower cloud will also impede navigation. The combination of these factors will require the highest standards of airmanship to be adopted at a time when the demands on the pilot are far greater.

Prior to Descending

Be aware of the location of any obstructions such as TV masts and HT cables which may not be marked on your chart. Remember that there may be obstacles up to 299 feet high which do not have to be marked on the chart. Also it is worth remembering your fellow aviators in other forms of aircraft: i.e. helicopters, hot air balloons, hang-gliders and paragliders, gliders and even microlight aircraft who could all be operating down at the low level that you have selected. High ground which is below 500 feet may also be missing from your chart and if there is a tall mast on top of a hill *(the usual situation for them!)* you could have little or no clearance from that obstacle. On your map, a white area of up to 499' could have an obstruction up to 299' unmarked ie. 798'.

Carry out a careful **FREDA** check before descending, especially paying attention to the engine instruments and noting the altimeter setting. Any altimeter error could reduce your margin from the ground.

At low level the effect of drift and your passage relative to the ground is very pronounced particularly when turning into or downwind. Also your apparent speed is very noticeable. You may appear to be skidding or slipping across the ground and you must beware this misleading impression and ensure that you continue to fly the aircraft in balance with the ball centred. A tailwind will give the impression of higher speed than usual and can tempt you to try to slow down, Reducing airspeed when you are already slow *(having set up your slow safe cruise)* would be extremely dangerous especially at low level as there would be insufficient height or time to recover from a stall if inadvertently entered.

A headwind is the reverse. Here there is no temptation to slow down so the situation is not as dangerous. The sideways drift due to a crosswind may confuse you when trying to turn as there could be a temptation to use more or less rudder than really required. Again this skid or slip will reduce the aircraft's performance and could be dangerous if the airspeed is allowed to degrade too far.

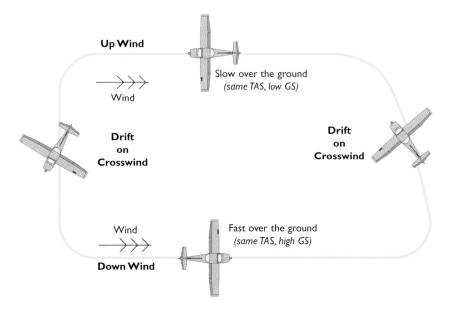

The effect of rain droplets can also lead to difficulties as the refraction off the droplets reduces visibility. Haze is another problem which can severely reduce forward visibility, especially when flying into sun.

Turbulence and Windshear

Turbulence and windshear are both common close to the ground because of the effect of surface friction and changes in windspeed or direction. Convection currents are also present especially on hot days. To some extent you will already have experienced these effects every time you come in to land at the airfield, but the effect is fairly short-lived. Sustained turbulence and gusts can be fatiguing and proper precautions should be adopted. Be aware that any passengers are more likely to suffer nausea if they are being bumped around and keep the cabin well ventilated. It is also worth keeping one hand on the throttle to be ready for any required power changes to counteract a gust.

Aircraft Configuration

If the visibility is good there is no need to adopt the '**slow safe cruise**' configuration, but in poor visibility or where good manoeuvrability is required it is better to lower some flap and set up the slow safe cruise configuration. This also improves the forward visibility and enables better controllability to be achieved, due to the extra power causing a greater slipstream effect. Unfortunately the increased drag from having flap extended for some time will increase the fuel consumption which may be another consideration as range will be reduced.

AIRMANSHIP

It is imperative to maintain a very good lookout for other aircraft and obstacles, including the feathered variety *(there will be more birdlife at lower levels and a birdstrike is always unwelcome)*. Be a good neighbour. Operating at low level and possibly with a higher power setting *(if in the slow safe cruise configuration)* can be annoying for people and animals. Select your practice areas carefully and avoid breaching rule 5. The lower you are flying, the more difficult it will be to attend to the other important tasks in the cockpit. Remember: **AVIATE - NAVIGATE - COMMUNICATE** *(the latter may be difficult at low level as you may be out of range of any ground station especially if there is a line of hills between the aircraft and the airfield.)*

Maintain good control at all times and a high awareness of factors such as drift, paying attention to your airspeed. Do not make turns at large angles of bank. Consider switching on strobes or landing lights to improve the chance of other aircraft seeing you. Make an early decision to land.

Quiz No. 18b

1. Reasons for flying at low level could include: ...., ... a field prior to a .... or planned entry into the ......

2. At low level, there are hazards such as ...... and ......

3. Misleading effects of ...... and ...... are more pronounced at low level.

4. Other problems which affect control of the aeroplane include ...... & .....

Answers
No. 18b

1. Deteriorating Weather, Inspecting,
   Precautionary Landing, VFR Entry and Exit Lanes.
2. TV Masts, HT Cables.
3. Skidding, Slipping.
4. Turbulence, Windshear.

Chapter 18 - *Exercise 18c*

Radio Navigation - VOR

18c. LESSON AIM

To learn how to use the VOR.

LESSON OBJECTIVE

By the end of the lesson you will be able to use the main features of the VOR accurately to aid visual navigation.

AIRMANSHIP

Lookout. Location. Frequencies. MORSE CODE. Warning Flags.

Introduction

The theory of the VHF Omni-directional Radio Range (**VOR**) is covered in Volume 3 of this series. This section is concerned with the practical application. The bearing information provided by the VOR is based on a VHF transmission and thus is more accurate than ADF or VDF *(dealt with later in the chapter)*. Information about frequencies and times and area of operational coverage are to be found in the AIP. You should always check this before using the VOR as the transmitter might be switched off or subject to limitations, which are not apparent from your chart. Ensure that you are within the designated operational coverage (**DOC**) (**UKAIP-COM**) of the VOR and that you are within "**line of sight**", i.e. there are no large hills between the aircraft and the transmitter which would affect the reception of the signal.

The aircraft equipment consists of a receiver and control panel and a display (or indicator).

Select the correct frequency for the chosen VOR on the receiver and then turn the selector knob to **IDENT**. This allows you to hear the Morse code *(usually three letters)* identification signal to enable you to verify that you have selected the correct beacon. *(It is worth writing down the morse ident on your PLOG before flight)* Since the range of available frequencies for VORs is a fairly narrow band, it is common to find VORs with very similar frequencies in the same locality and therefore it is easy to make a mistake.

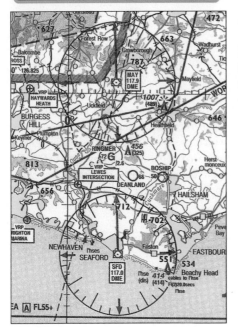

Example:

MAY (Mayfield) has the frequency 117.90 and almost due South is SFD (Seaford) on 117.00.

Make sure that the warning flag *(NAV or OFF)* is not showing and then turn the OBS *(omni-bearing selector)* knob to centre the CDI *(course deviation indicator)*. The number showing at the top of the indicator will be the radial you are on, if the FROM flag is showing. If the TO flag is showing then the number at the bottom of the display will indicate the radial you are on.

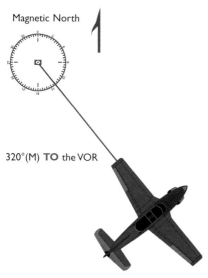

Magnetic North

320°(M) **TO** the VOR

To determine your course from your preset position **TO** a VOR station, tune into the station and turn the OBS knob until the CDI needle centres with a **TO** indication.

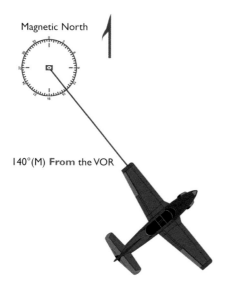

Magnetic North

140°(M) **From** the VOR

To determine your present direction **FROM** a VOR station, tune into the station and turn the OBS knob until the CDI needle centres with a **FROM** indication.

Intercepting a Chosen Radial

To plan to intercept and follow a specific radial, first determine your position relative to the desired track. Set the reciprocal of the radial which is the inbound course. The CDI will be deflected showing you which way to turn to intercept the track. Your choice of intercept angle depends on a number of factors. The shortest intercept would be via a 90° intercept, but as soon as the CDI started to move you would have to start to turn to reduce the intercept to establish on the track. More usually an intercept angle of 30, 45 or 60° would be selected. If you are very close to the VOR station the CDI will move very quickly but if you are a long distance away from it then it will move more slowly. Consider the 1 in 60 rule to understand this point:

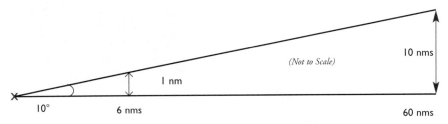

(Not to Scale)

10° 6 nms 1 nm 10 nms 60 nms

In reducing the angle of intercept, it is helpful to use a technique of halving the intercept when the CDI needle reaches half-scale deflection and continue to reduce the intercept in this manner until the CDI is exactly centred, with good judgment, as you turn onto the track.

Tracking to or from a VOR

When tracking to a VOR, once intercepted, check that the correct QDM is set under the course index and check that the TO flag is showing. The VOR is a command instrument and therefore if the CDI needle is to the right then fly right, if it is to the left of centre, then fly left. If there is no wind, then the heading equal to the inbound track will enable you to fly to the VOR. If there is any element of crosswind, then heading corrections will be required to keep the CDI needle centred. Use only small heading corrections initially and wait for the needle to move back into the centre. This method of waiting for the CDI needle to stabilise is called **"bracketing"**. If the needle remains in the same position, but is still off-centre then the wind correction angle has been achieved, but you will still need to make a heading correction to regain track. As you track towards the VOR station the needle movement may become very erratic close to the station. At the passage over the station, the nav warning flag will appear just after the TO/FROM flag has flickered. This shows that you are in the cone of confusion directly overhead the station. To track outbound, i.e. away from the VOR, you should set the required radial on the course index and check that the FROM flag is showing. As before, if the CDI is to the right, then fly right and if it is to the left, then fly left, by a small amount until the CDI needle is centred.

Obtaining a VOR Position Fix

This is a useful way of backing up your visual navigation. Where possible, select two VORs which give as near to a 90 degree cut. Identify each of the two stations, then centre the CDIs with the FROM flag showing. This procedure will enable you to see the radials on which the aircraft is located. Plot the two lines on your chart and where they cross you will have a fix. If you then estimate your position you can determine whether the fix makes sense. Beware, it is easy to select a radial 180 degrees out if you do not ensure that the FROM flag is showing.

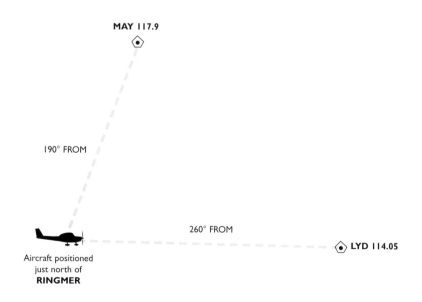

LESSON AIM

To learn how to use the VOR, to assist in Visual Navigation.

LESSON OBJECTIVE

By the end of the lesson you will be able to fly to and away from the VOR and also fix your position.

AIRMANSHIP

Lookout. Location. Frequencies. Morse Code.

AIR EXERCISE   *To Fly the VOR.*

Teaching Points

Tracking TO a VOR

1) Once intercepted, check **TO** flag is showing and the correct QDM is set under course index.
2) If CDI to the right, fly right, if CDI to the left, fly left, to intercept required track.
3) Assess drift and adjust heading accordingly. **Fly the DI not the CDI.**

Tracking FROM the VOR

1) SID.
2) Select required magnetic track on course index.
3) Check the **FROM** flag is showing.
4) If CDI right, fly right, if CDI left, fly left.

Intercepting a Chosen Radial

1) SID.
2) If tracking **TO** the station, select the required magnetic track inbound using the OBS. Check that the **TO** flag is showing.
3) Steer heading to intercept chosen radial eg. track ±30/45/60.
4) Monitor rate of track closure and aim to turn on track with needle centred.

Obtaining a VOR Position Fix

1) Select 2 VORs as close to a 90° cut as possible.
2) Frequency and ident check.
3) Rotate OBS to centre the CDI with **FROM** flag showing.
4) Plot radial on chart and repeat with second VOR to give fix.
5) Estimate your position.
6) Does it make sense?

Select*(correct frequency)* • **Ident** • **Display**
(bearing & radial selected & display in correct sense)

Fuel • Radio • Engine • DI • Altimeter (FREDA Checks)

Chapter 18 - *Exercise 18c*

Radio Navigation - ADF

18c. **LESSON AIM**

To learn to use the ADF equipment fitted to the aircraft.

LESSON OBJECTIVE

By the end of the lesson you will be able to use the main features of the ADF accurately to assist you in visual radio navigation and to home to and from an NDB.

AIRMANSHIP

Lookout. Location. Frequencies. Range. Limitations.

Introduction

The principles of the working of the ADF are set out in Volume 3. The Non-directional beacon (**NDB**) is a ground based transmitter which transmits radio energy in all directions. The airborne system in the aircraft is called the Automatic Direction Finder (**ADF**). The indicator *(needle)* on the ADF points towards the tuned NDB. As with the VOR, the frequencies and promulgated ranges of the NDBs are published in the AIP. You must check that the NDB is within range, select the correct frequency and then identify the beacon by listening to the Morse code *(usually two or three letters)*. The final check is that the ADF is indeed operating or "**ADFing**". To do this select the ANT setting on the receiver. This should cause the needle to rotate to the 3 o'clock position on the dial. Switching to ADF on the dial will then cause the needle to point directly at the beacon.

Tracking to the Beacon

The equipment in the aircraft will usually be in the form of a Relative Bearing Indicator (**RBI**), although in better equipped aircraft it may be a Radio Magnetic Indicator (**RMI** – *see Volume 3 for more detail*). Since the needle on the RBI will always point at the beacon, regardless of the orientation of the aircraft, it is necessary to calculate the relative bearing of the aircraft from the beacon in order to determine the heading to fly. The relative bearing is the angle between the heading of the aircraft and the direction of the NDB. Orientation is achieved by adding the magnetic heading to the relative bearing and if the total exceeds 360, subtracting 360 from the total. This is known as the QDM. The reciprocal is the QDR and is calculated by subtracting 180 from the QDM. Another way of calculating the QDM is to use a pencil to parallel the needle and then superimpose this onto the DI.

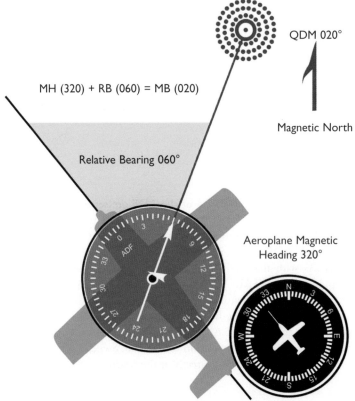

QDM 020°

MH (320) + RB (060) = MB (020)

Magnetic North

Relative Bearing 060°

Aeroplane Magnetic
Heading 320°

NB. By mentally superimposing the ADF needle on top of the
Direction Indicator this will show you QDM and QDR.

Another way of working out the QDM is using a rotatable compass card. In some RBIs it is possible to turn the compass card manually to "**slave**" it to the direction indicator and if this is done so that the heading is set at the top against the index mark, the QDM is easily read off the RBI indicator.

To track towards the beacon it will be necessary to make allowances for the wind or else the path flown to reach the NDB will be a curved one. If the needle starts to point out to the right, then turn right.

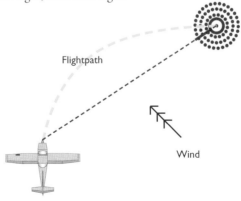

A technique called **'bracketing'** can be used to correct for drift. This is illustrated below.

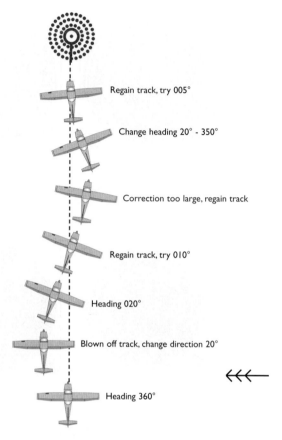

Regain track, try 005°

Change heading 20° - 350°

Correction too large, regain track

Regain track, try 010°

Heading 020°

Blown off track, change direction 20°

Heading 360°

Tracking Away from the Beacon

As you approach the beacon, the needle will start to become more and more sensitive. You can judge how accurately you have tracked to the beacon by monitoring the speed at which the needle falls – if it is very quick then you have probably passed directly overhead. Once you have passed over the beacon, the head of the needle will be pointing back towards the beacon. It is easier to think in terms of turning towards the head to make corrections rather than trying to calculate the information that the tail of the needle is telling you. Thus needle pointing left, turn left and vice versa.

Since the ADF needle always points towards the station, the easiest way to reach the beacon is to fly with the needle constantly at the top of the indicator. This procedure is known as homing. Turn the aircraft in the direction of the needle until it points to the top of the indicator and then keep it there. Of course the wind will tend to blow you off track and then as you correct to keep the needle at the top, your path will tend to become curved.

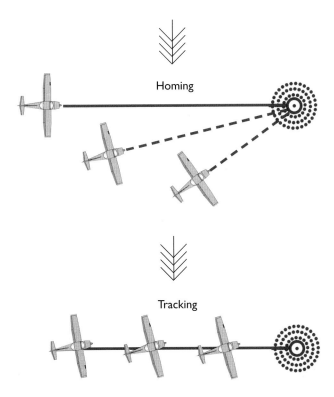

Homing

Tracking

LESSON AIM

To Learn to use the ADF equipment fitted to the aeroplane, to assist your visual navigation.

LESSON OBJECTIVE

By the end of the lesson you will be accurately to use the main features of the ADF to permit safe radio navigation and to home to track to an NDB.

AIRMANSHIP   Lookout. Location. Frequencies. Range. Limitations.

AIR EXERCISE   *To Fly the ADF.*

Teaching Points

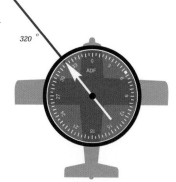

Tracking to the Beacon

1) SID and regular Compass DI Checks are required.
2) Orientate the aeroplane and fly the heading to intercept the chosen radial/QDM.
3) Once the radial has been intercepted, initially fly the same heading as track.
4) If the head of the needle moves LEFT the aeroplane is RIGHT of track.
5) If the head of the needle is 10° LEFT, turn LEFT say 20° (Track -20°).
6) Fly the new heading until the needle shows +20°.
7) Turn the aeroplane back onto track and allow for drift.

Tracking from the Beacon

1) Use the same procedure as above, however, the needle now points back.

Points to Remember

1) If the head of the needle moves LEFT - Turn Left.
2) If the head of the needle moves RIGHT - Turn Right.
3) Regular FREDA Checks.

Select*(correct frequency)* • **Ident** • **Display**
(bearing & radial selected & display in correct sense)

Fuel • Radio • Engine • DI • Altimeter (FREDA Checks)

Introduction

The DME is often co-located with a VOR and can provide you with very useful information, particularly as regards position fixing. A slant range is measured and this is presented in the cockpit as a digital readout. Since the DME is often paired with the VOR it can provide the distance to the VOR and also be used for making a more accurate fix. The position line obtained from the DME will be circular and it can be used to resolve any ambiguities which may arise with a **VOR FIX**.

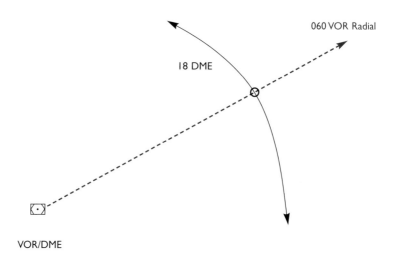

As with all other radio navigation aids, the AIP should be checked for frequencies, promulgated range and any other operational constraints. The frequency should be selected and then identified positively by listening to the Morse code. Often this will be the same code as the VOR but at a higher pitched sound. The Morse ident will only sound every 30 seconds as opposed to the VOR ident which sounds every 10 seconds.

VHF/DF (Direction Finding)

| 18c. **LESSON AIM** |
| To learn to use the procedures of VHF direction finding. |

| **LESSON OBJECTIVE** |
| By the end of the lesson you will be able to use the procedures and services of VHF direction finding to assist you in visual navigation. |

| **AIRMANSHIP** |
| Lookout. Location. Frequencies. |

Introduction

At certain airfields, a VDF service may be available. On charts this may be marked but you should of course, check the AIP. The equipment required is located at the airfield and no special equipment other than a radio is needed in the aeroplane.

LESSON AIM

To Learn to use the procedures of VHF Direction Finding.

LESSON OBJECTIVE

By the end of the lesson you will be able to to use the procedures and services of VHF Direction Finding accurately to assist you in your Visual Navigation.

AIRMANSHIP

Lookout. Location. Frequencies.

AIR EXERCISE   *To Fly a QDM and Homing, back to an Airfield.*

Teaching Points

1) Use of VHF Direction Finding.
2) Availability, AIP, Frequencies.
3) R/T Procedures and ATC liaison.
4) Obtaining a QDM and Homing.

VDF Bearings

1) QDM Magnetic Bearing **To** the Station.
2) QDR Magnetic Bearing **From** the Station (reciprocal of QDM).
3) QTE True Bearing **From** the Station.

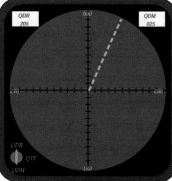

Golf Mike Whisky
Request QDM

VDF STATION

Golf Mike Whisky
QDM zero two five

QDM 025

The controller will be equipped with a digital read-out which shows a bearing of the aircraft from the station. Since the controller may not be looking at the equipment at the time when you call for the bearing, it is usual to make a radio call to alert him, by specifically requesting the information. Although in theory there are several bearings you could request from a controller, i.e. QDM, QDR or QTE *(explained further below)*, in practice these days VDF is rarely used other than to obtain a QDM for homing to a station. When making your call to the VDF station therefore, you should give your call sign and then "**request QDM**" followed by your full callsign again. Sometimes the controller will ask you to transmit "**for DF**". In these circumstances you should transmit your full call sign slowly adding the words "**transmitting for DF**".

QDM

The QDM is the magnetic bearing to the station and in nil wind conditions will be the heading to steer direct to the station. To track to the station when there is a crosswind you will need to counter the drift. It would be normal to request a new QDM every half-minute or so to update the tracking and if necessary you would modify the heading.

Exercise 18c — Radio Navigation VHF/DF

Teaching Points

Modern Equipment is generally accurate to ±2°, however accuracy may be decreased by:

VDF Site Errors
Such as Reflection from nearby uneven ground, buildings, aircraft or vehicles.

VHF Propagation Errors
Caused by irregular propagation over differing terrain, especially if the aeroplane is at long range from the VDF ground station.

VDF Bearing Accuracy

Class A   Accurate to within ±2°.

Class B   Accurate to within ±5°.

Class C   Accurate to within ±10°.

Class D   Less Accurate than Class C, CAP 46 lists some Class D VDF Stations with accuracy in excess of ±10°.

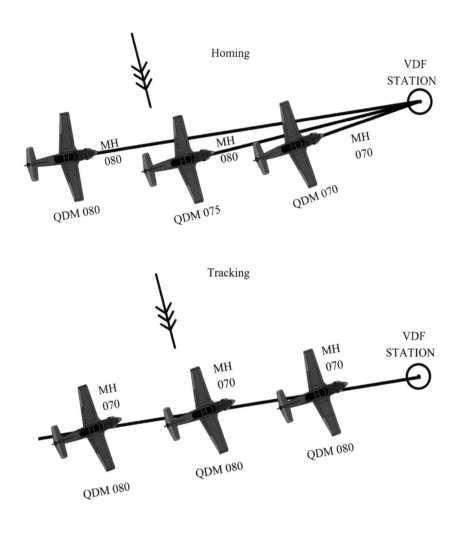

QDR

The QDR is the magnetic bearing from the station and can be used to orientate yourself, in a similar way to the radial from a VOR.

QTE

This is the true bearing from a station, which would be used to plot a position line from the station to the aircraft on your chart. This is rarely used these days but was common before the wide availability of radio navigation equipment.

Bearing Accuracy

The classification of bearing accuracy is as follows:

Class A **Accurate to within +/- 2°**

Class B **Accurate to within +/- 5°**

Class C **Accurate to within +/- 10°**

Class D **Less accurate than Class C.**

(there are a number of these stations listed in CAP46)

All of the forms of radio navigation set out in this section should be used simply as an adjunct to your visual navigation and not as a substitute for proper map reading. If you rely totally on a radio navigation aid and have no back-up then when the radio aid is suddenly out of service or the equipment fails you are left with no options. Therefore use the radio aids to confirm position and assist your visual navigation. After all, that is what they are: Radio Aids!

Radio Navigation En-route
& Terminal Radar

18C. LESSON AIM

To learn the use of en-route/terminal radar.

LESSON OBJECTIVE

By the end of the lesson you will be able to use the procedures and services of en-route/terminal radar accurately to assist you in visual navigation.

AIRMANSHIP

Lookout, Location, airspace, (prohibited, controlled, restricted) and safe altitudes. Frequencies.

Introduction

The term radar stands for Radio detection and ranging. In the en route and terminal environment, the use of radar greatly enhances the air traffic controller's ability to provide safe separation and fix an aircraft's position. In addition, it reduces the amount of air-ground communication and allows the controller to steer aircraft around obstacles *(such as other aircraft)* by providing radar vectors.

Radio works by transmission of electromagnetic energy in the form of radio waves, which can carry information such as speech or Morse code, from one transmitter to a number of receivers. Electromagnetic energy reflects from certain types of surface. Radar works by measuring the elapsed time between the transmission of a pulse of radio energy and the time it returns to the source as an echo. This measurement enables the distance of the object from the antenna to be calculated.

En route radar is often designated as **LARS** *(Lower Airspace Radar Service)*. It is necessary for the pilot to request the service and this is covered in more detail in volume 5 on Communications in this series. Primary radar does not require any special equipment in the aircraft beyond a radio. The controller has the radar which will usually be in the form of a beam which he can tilt upwards to detect the aircraft. If the aircraft is not within his beam he will not detect it.

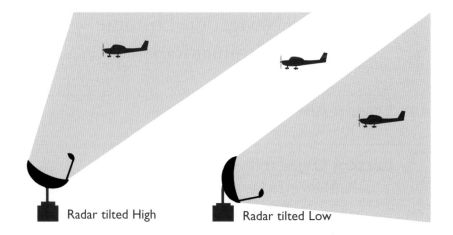

Radar tilted High   Radar tilted Low

Availability

The frequencies and availability of radar services are listed in the appropriate section of the AIP. Some LARS frequencies are marked on the chart. If you are planning to use a military frequency bear in mind that many of them are closed at weekends.

RT Procedures and ATC Liaison

It is likely that the air traffic service offering radar will use a callsign "**Radar**" or "**Approach**". Make a specific request for the service you wish to use:

Radar Advisory Service (RAS): You will be provided with details of all traffic and given avoidance action to take. If you elect not to take the action then you must tell the controller. Note: RAS will only be supplied to aircraft operating under instrument flight rules so you need to ensure that compliance with any ATC instructions does not place you in IMC.

Radar Information Service (RIS): You will be provided with details of other traffic and it is up to you to decide on any avoiding action.

Radar Vectors: these may be given to you by the radar controller to identify which aircraft you are and also to enable him to steer you around conflicting traffic. You should maintain such headings until given another heading to fly or until told to "resume your own navigation".

Pilot's Responsibilities

Whilst using a radar service you remain responsible for terrain clearance, you should also remain in VMC and know where you are. If the controller tells you to resume your own navigation after a number of radar vectors, but you are unsure of your location, do not hesitate to ask for assistance.

Secondary Surveillance Radar (SSR)

Exercise 18c Radio Navigation En-route & Terminal Radar

Function Selector Knob
Enables the crew to aelect the various operating modes.

Off
Switches off the transponder.

SBY
Allows the transponder to warm up ready for use.

On
Transmits the selected code in Mode 'A' (Aeroplane identification mode).

Alt
Altitude reporting capability Mode 'C' (if fitted to the aeroplane).

TST
Tests the correct operation of the transponder by generating a self interrogation signal. Success illuminates the reply monitor light (some models).

Code Selection Knobs
Numbers from 0-7.

Reply Monitor Light
Flashes to indicate the transponder's response to interrogation.

Ident Button (Switch)
Allows positive identification by radar controller, squawk ident.

Special Transponder Codes

2000 Crossing International Boundary.
7000 Conspicuity.
7500 Unlawful Interference or Hijack.
7600 Radio Failure.
7700 Emergency.

Primary radar has a number of limitations and suffers from problems such as ground clutter and weather clutter. Even rain can cause a problem. Secondary radar overcomes a lot of these problems. This system requires equipment in the aircraft in the form of a transponder. The SSR transmits a series of coded pulses on one frequency which are received by any transponder which is in range. It then responds with a different set of coded pulses on a different frequency. In the aircraft, the equipment *(depicted above)* will be set with a code of four numbers. The controller will give you the code to set and this will be displayed on his radar screen, next to the primary return for the aircraft. The controller's job is thus simplified as he can easily identify each aircraft by its own code. You can see from the diagram that there are several function knobs and using these you can select the required setting. If your transponder has the capability for altitude reporting (**Mode C (ALT)**) you may be asked to select this as it will enable the controller to monitor your altitude.

Additionally there are a number of other codes which may be set. You will recall these from your Air Law studies:

7700	**Emergency (Mayday)**
7600	**Radio Failure**
7500	**Hijack or Unlawful Interference**
7000	**Conspicuity**
7004	**Aerobatics**

The advantage of using the transponder is that if you were to become lost it would be very easy for the radar controller to locate you by giving you a specific code to set (**"squawk"**). If you fly into controlled airspace you are likely to be required to squawk and your instructor will ensure that you practise these procedures before you carry out your qualifying cross country flight.

Quiz No. 18c

1. Before using a VOR, you should .... and ....

2. Centring the CDI needle enables the ..... to be read off the indicator.

3. As you pass over the VOR station, ... flag will be displayed.

4. An NDB is a ...... transmitter and the ADF is ....

5. The ADF equipment in a light aircraft is usually a ......

6. If no allowance is made for drift when tracking towards an NDB, the aircraft will be ......

7. DME is used to measure ......

8. VHF Direction Finding can be achieved using a ......

9. Bearing accuracy in VDF or DF is classified using Class .... to Class .... Class B is accurate within ....

10. SSR stands for ....

11. If you suffer radio failure you should select a special code of ...... on your transponder.

12. 7700 is a code used to denote ......

Answers
No. 18c

1.   Select the Correct Frequency, Ident the Morse Code.
2.   Radial (QDM, QDR).
3.   Navigation Warning.
4.   Ground-based, the Airborne Equipment.
5.   Relative Bearing Indicator.
6.   Homing.
7.   Slant Range.
8.   Radio Only.
9.   A, D, ± 5°.
10.   Secondary Surveillance Radar.
11.   7600.
12.   An Emergency or Mayday.

Chapter 19 - *Exercise 19*

Basic Instrument Appreciation

19. LESSON AIM

To learn the sensation of flight with sole reference to the instruments and with no external references.

LESSON OBJECTIVE

By the end of the lesson you will be able accurately and safely to use the instruments to fly basic manoeuvres without outside reference.

AIRMANSHIP

Spatial disorientation. Physiological sensation. IFR rules. Minimum safe altitudes. (MSA).

Introduction

Up until now your flying has all been visual, concentrating on flying the correct attitudes by reference to the horizon and other external features. You have mainly used your eyes to select the correct attitude, backed up by a brief cross-referencing of appropriate instruments to check for accuracy. Your work cycle has been: **Lookout, Attitude, Instruments.** You have focussed on Lookout, although in some manoeuvres you will have been aware of sensations which might have conflicted with the information which your eyes were giving you. Particularly in accelerating flight when you have experienced 'g', your bodily sensations will have changed from when you are in level flight. If you then close your eyes, the information about which way up you are will be generated by a combination of the feeling of your body pressing down on the seat and the balance mechanism in your ears. You would find that you become disorientated extremely quickly with your eyes shut if you try to detect the movements of the aircraft.

It is because of this that you will need to become acquainted with the detailed information which can be provided by the instruments and to learn to rely on the information provided to you visually. Since your body may be giving you conflicting information, you must learn to trust your eyes and what is showing on the instruments. *(see Volume 5 on Human Factors for more detail on disorientation and the illusions experienced in instrument flying).*

Your instructor will demonstrate to you some of the effects, by asking you to close your eyes whilst he puts the aircraft into various *(gentle)* manoeuvres. He will ask you to describe what is happening and after a minute or two you will be asked to open your eyes. You are very likely to be extremely surprised about the attitude of the aircraft. This should reinforce the message that your eyes are vital for instrument flying.

The introduction to instrument flying which forms a part of your PPL course is not intended to equip you to fly with sole reference to instruments. However it is intended to allow you to appreciate the difficulties associated with flying on instruments in order that you realise that a lot more training is required to enable you to carry out the procedures effectively. It is a well-documented fact that a large proportion of the fatal accidents suffered in light aircraft are due to pilots flying into instrument meteorological conditions (**IMC**) without adequate training. Remember that your licence is for flight in VMC only. It is not only illegal but also highly dangerous, to fly in conditions outside those for which you are trained.

LESSON AIM

To understand the sensation of flight with sole reference to the instruments and with no external visual reference.

LESSON OBJECTIVE

By the end of the lesson you will be able accurately and safely to use the instruments to fly basic manoeuvres without outside reference.

AIRMANSHIP

Spatial disorientation. Physiological Sensation. Instrument Flight Rules. Minimum Safe Altitudes. (MSA).

AIR EXERCISE — *Instrument Interpretation. Disorientation. Straight & Level at various Airspeeds & Configurations. Climbing & Descending, Standard Turns, Turning onto selected Headings.*

Teaching Points

The Causes of Poor Instrument Flying are:

1) Poor and/or incorrect method of reading the instrument panel.
2) Not understanding the information given by the instruments (singly and collectively).
3) Heavy control inputs.
4) Poor application of power/attitude flight techniques to achieve the required aeroplane performance.
5) Not fully trusting the instruments and trying to use your senses.
6) Poor trimming.
7) Not relaxing.

Power + Attitude
= Performance

Selective Radial Scan

Primary Scan

Secondary Scan

Work Cycles: **Power • Attitude • Trim & Select • Hold • Trim**

Attitude Flying

Instrument flying is a combination of understanding and interpreting the information on the instruments, continually scanning them to follow trends and then applying that information to the selection of the correct power setting and attitude for the required manoeuvre. This is often called "attitude instrument flying" and is based on the concept we have met before:

Power + Attitude = Performance

In determining the attitude to select it is necessary to realise that attitude can mean pitch attitude or bank attitude. You then need to understand what information about attitude is being provided by the various instruments. It is also important to understand that any power change will affect the attitude of the aircraft and will result in a change of flightpath or airspeed.

Exercise 19   Basic Instrument Flight, Part 2 of 4

The Main Instrument

Attitude Indicator Display

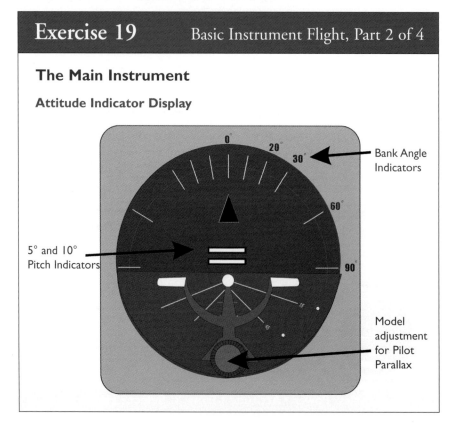

Bank Angle Indicators

5° and 10° Pitch Indicators

Model adjustment for Pilot Parallax

Although you have become familiar with the information displayed on some of the instruments such as the ASI, Altimeter and DI, there may be aspects of the Attitude Indicator (**AI**), sometimes called the Artificial Horizon, with which you are not yet fully conversant. On the diagram above you will see that there is a model aircraft which represents the aircraft, with the centre dot representing the nose of the aircraft. There are also pitch indicators and bank angle indicators marked. The line across the middle represents the horizon and the blue area is the sky with the dark area representing the ground or sea. Different models vary slightly, but your instructor will explain the meaning of the different markings on the instrument in your training aircraft.

You will practise selecting pitch attitudes using the elevators as usual but comparing the apparently small movement required when selecting pitch on the AI as compared with the visual selection of pitch referring to the natural horizon. Initially you may find that you select too large a pitch attitude but after some practice you will become more familiar with the indications. Likewise you will practise selecting bank angles with ailerons, using the bank angle indicators to select various bank attitudes. You will find that increasing bank angle makes it more difficult to maintain the pitch of the aircraft, particularly since the dot of the model aircraft is very small. Since the apparent movements of the model aircraft are so small relative to the instrument, you will move the model, by only a bar's width or less *(the bar representing the wings of the aircraft).*

Because you can select both pitch and bank with a great deal of accuracy by reference to the AI, it is often known as the Master Instrument. When scanning the other instruments for information, you will return always to the AI to check the attitude of the aircraft. Selecting the correct attitude to achieve the required performance is also about selecting the correct power setting. The rpm gauge therefore becomes your other '**control**' instrument as it enables you *(with the AI)* to select and maintain the performance required. The other instruments are the '**performance instruments**'. Having selected the correct power and attitude, you will then cross-check the actual performance, i.e. altimeter for altitude, DI for heading, ASI for airspeed. You will learn to scan the main six instruments *(depicted above)* by focussing on the AI as your Master instrument and radiating out to the others in turn. The Selective Radial Scan is dealt with further on the next page.

Control Sequence

Control Sequence

1) Visualise the desired new Flight Path and Airspeed.
2) **Select** the Attitude on AI and the Power required to achieve the desired performance by moving the controls, and then checking when the aeroplane has achieved the estimated attitude on the AI.
3) **Hold** the Attitude on the AI, allowing the aeroplane to settle down into its new performance, and allowing the pressure instruments that experience some lag to catch up.
4) Make small adjustments to Attitude and Power until the actual performance equals the desired performance.
5) **Trim**, which is essential if you are to achieve accurate and comfortable instrument flight. Heavy loads can be trimmed off earlier in the sequence to assist in control, if desired; however, remember that the function of trim is to relieve control pressures on the pilot, not to change aircraft attitude.

Simple Scan for Straight & Level

Instructor will explain the expansion of the Simple Scan.

Simple Scan for Turning

Work Cycles: **Power • Attitude • Trim** & **Select • Hold • Trim**

278

In addition to the above, be careful not to '**over-control**'. Making large or fast inputs on instruments leads to an uneven flightpath, requiring more corrections. Make sure that the aircraft is correctly and accurately trimmed. Remain relaxed and do not allow yourself to be distracted from the scan of the instruments, returning always to the Master instrument after each task such as changing radio frequency etc.

Selective Radial Scan

The selective radial scan is so called because the pilot selects the required instruments to give him the necessary information for each manoeuvre, then radiates out from the Master instrument and briefly scans the instrument to derive the required information before returning to the AI. Before developing the selective radial scan, it is important to understand the information that you can derive from each instrument. The attitude indicator will give you the direct information that you require for pitch and bank, but it does not show any yaw or balance. Thus your eyes must move down to the balance ball briefly before returning to the AI.

The DI will provide direct information about heading as will the compass. Radiate out from the AI to select the required instrument before returning the gaze to the AI. These two instruments are also providing indirect information about bank. The ASI should be checked in the same way by radiating out from the AI and then back. In addition to the direct information about airspeed, the ASI is giving you indirect information about pitch. The altimeter also gives you indirect information about pitch in addition to the direct information about altitude. The VSI is a trend instrument showing rate of climb or descent, but indirectly pitch of the aircraft.

These instruments are the performance instruments. In order to achieve the selective radial scan, you should use the AI as the master instrument. Radiate your eyes out from the AI to the required instruments for each manoeuvre, returning between each instrument to the AI.

Scan for Straight and Level Flight

The basic scan for straight and level flight *(also known as the primary scan)* is centred on the AI and radiates out to the DI to check heading *(i.e. straight)* and then back to the AI before scanning across to the altimeter to check and confirm altitude *(i.e. level).*

The secondary scan should include occasional glances at the ASI and the balance ball. Do not get fixated on one instrument and do not allow the radial scan to break down. If you fixate on one instrument it will tend to lead to delayed recognition of a deviation from the desired flightpath. Naturally you will need to move your gaze to the rpm gauge when making power adjustments or the temperature and pressure gauges when carrying out a cruise check, but return immediately to the radial scan once the desired information has been obtained.

Select power as normal for the climb or descent and then pitch the nose to the appropriate attitude using the AI. For a normal climb this will be about the 10-degree pitch line above the horizon. For a descent it will be about one wing bar width of the miniature aeroplane below the horizon.

Exercise 19 — Basic Instrument Flight, Part 4 of 4

Simple Scan for Climbing & Descending

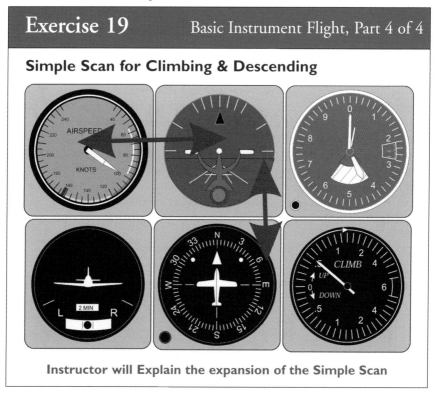

Instructor will Explain the expansion of the Simple Scan

The basic scan in both cases is **AI-ASI-AI-DI**. Once established in the climb or descent, then the secondary scan will include the VSI and balance ball. You only need to include the altimeter in the scan when you start to approach the desired altitude. Levelling off is as you would expect, from the climb ie, Attitude, Power Trim. Select the correct attitude for straight and level flight, glance at the rpm gauge to select cruise power and then trim. Revert to the straight and level scan and make any small adjustments as necessary. When levelling off from the descent it is of course: Power, Attitude, Trim. Apply the required power and check to confirm on the rpm gauge, then select the attitude for straight and level flight on the AI, trim and then adjust and check, reverting to the straight and level scan.

Turning

Normally turns on instruments will be limited to rate one or approximately 15° of bank in your training aeroplane. *(To calculate rate one turns, see page 122.)* This is because it is more difficult to control the attitude of the aircraft in pitch when increased angles of bank are selected, as pitch would be solely by reference to the dot on the AI. Once the aircraft symbol has been banked, the wings of the miniature aeroplane are no longer aligned with the horizon line.

Roll into the turn using the AI to select the bank angle or the Turn coordinator to select a rate one turn. Apply a small amount of back pressure and balance with rudder as normal. Your primary scan will therefore be: AI-Turn coordinator and ball-Altimeter. Once established in the turn use the VSI to ensure that you are remaining level as this will show you deviations in pitch more readily than the altimeter. Only include the DI in the scan as you approach the required heading. Anticipate rolling out from the turn about 10 degrees before the required heading and using the AI, roll the wings level, release the back pressure and balance with rudder. Return to the straight and level scan. You should not trim during the manoeuvre as it is transient and therefore it should not be necessary to retrim on rolling level.

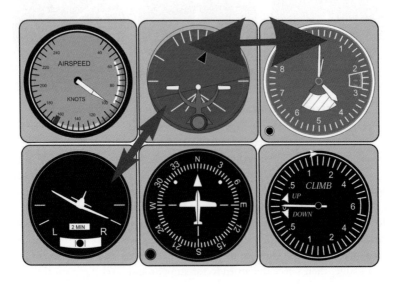

Instrument Checks

Before flight you should check the serviceability of all of the instruments. Pay particular attention to the working of the vacuum system *(as indicated by the suction gauge)* which is essential for the AI and DI and also the back-up electrical gyro system *(usually the Turn Coordinator)*. As part of the walk around you will have checked the pitot head and static vent to ensure that there are no obstructions.

Taxy Checks

During taxying, check that all of the required instruments are working correctly, by making turns sufficient to note the indications of each as follows:

Turn left and note the AI shows a turn to the left, the Turn Coordinator also shows a turn to the left, the balance ball skids out to the right. Then check that the DI and compass are decreasing in heading indication, the miniature aeroplane symbol should be remaining upright showing no roll indication. Conversely turning right there should be indications of turns to the right, a skid to the left and the heading should be increasing in numerical value. Again there should be no roll indication.

In Flight

As part of your normal **FREDA** (cruise) checks, check that the suction gauge and ammeter are indicating correctly. These instruments will give you an indication if there is a problem with the gyroscopic instruments. Unfortunately there is no warning system if there is a problem with the pressure instruments due to the static source becoming blocked, but if the temperature is very low and the possibility of ice forming is likely then you should turn on the pitot heater to help prevent ice blocking the pitot tube. Some aeroplanes such as the PA 38 or PA 28 are fitted with alternative static sources inside the cockpit but detection of a problem can be difficult, as the instrument indications which could provide any clues are sometimes slow to develop.

The main thing to remember is that you are not being trained to fly solely by reference to instruments and without the appropriate rating it is illegal for you to do so. It is also very dangerous and should therefore be avoided. The main purpose of this exercise will have been to show you that it is necessary to obtain further training to fly on instruments, and to enable you to return to visual conditions when flying in hazy visibility as can sometimes be the case when flying into direct sun.

Quiz No. 19

1. In Instrument Flying the Master Instrument is the ......

2. A Simple Scan for Straight and Level Flight is ......

3. In the Selective Radial Scan you should ...... from the ......

4. The Scan for Climbing or Descending should be ....

5. Before carrying out Instrument Flying you should pay particular attention to ...... of your instruments.

6. Check the Instruments during ......

7. Flying on Instruments in cloud .... be carried out .... a rating.

Answers No. 19

1. AI (Attitude Indicator)
2. AI - DI - AI - Altimeter.
3. Radiate Out, Master Instrument.
4. AI - DI - AI - ASI
5. The Serviceability.
6. Taxying.
7. Should Not, Without.

Chapter 20 - Part 1

Night Flying

Night Orientation

---

20. LESSON AIM

To learn how to operate the aircraft at night, both on the ground and in the air and night circuits.

LESSON OBJECTIVE

Recognition of deteriorating weather, windshear.

AIRMANSHIP

Lookout, Airfield licensed for night ops, pre-flight checks, use of torch, adaptation of night vision

---

Exercise 20   Night Navigation, Runway Lighting

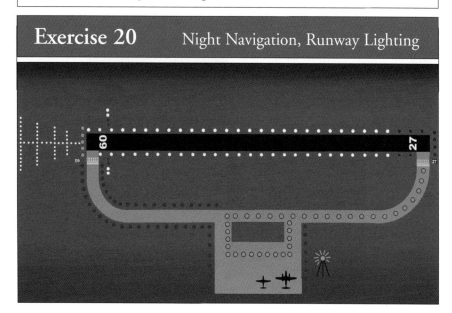

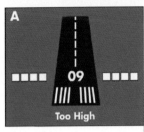

Too High

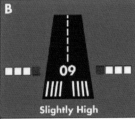

Slightly High

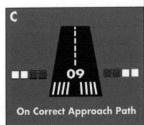

On Correct Approach Path

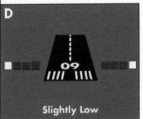

Slightly Low

Too Low

Planning

Before even checking the aeroplane, check the time that the airfield is scheduled to close and also any different procedures that may be in use at night. For instance, during the winter, some airfields may have different closing times on different days of the week to enable night flying to take place. There may be local rules relating to taxying the aircraft and if the taxiway is unlit you may have to back-track the runway.

Adapting your eyes to night vision is important. If you have not yet read the section in Volume 5 about the eyes, then do so now! It is best to avoid bright lighting just before night flying as it takes time for the eyes to adjust and therefore you should also be careful how you use your torch as carelessness can destroy your best night vision for up to half an hour. In addition to your normal equipment you should carry a torch and if possible use a torch with a red filter. Ensure that you carry spare batteries.

Pre Take-Off

Use your torch for the external checks of the aircraft, paying particular attention to all of the control surfaces and hinges. It is more difficult to see frost and ice and it is essential that all ice is cleared before night flight, as any ice present will not disperse in flight. Ensure that all tie-downs and chocks have been removed and stowed and also check the ground around the aircraft for suitability for taxying as it is more difficult to see from the aircraft in the dark.

It is a legal requirement that your navigation lights should all be serviceable. Although technically you do not have to have a serviceable landing light, taxying the aircraft without one is very tricky particularly if aerodrome lighting is minimal. Check that the cockpit lights are working and that the stall warner is serviceable.

Before start-up ensure that spare fuses are available and then place everything you will need within easy reach. Turn on sufficient cabin lighting without allowing it to be too bright. Ensure that the parking brakes are set, as it is more difficult to detect unwanted movement of the aircraft in the darkness. Warn people passing by that you are about to start up by flashing your landing lights on and off irregularly three or four times as well as switching on the red beacon. Shout out of the window "**clear prop**". Once the engine has started, check the electrical load is satisfactory and the system is charging.

You will be using more electrical services than during the day and the battery will drain much more quickly should the alternator fail. Check that the aircraft is not moving by looking out to the side, as it will be easier to detect movement than looking out to the front.

Taxying

Use the taxy light or landing light to assist in taxying, but exercise good airmanship and manners by avoiding dazzling other pilots or ground handling personnel such as marshallers. It is essential to taxy slowly and look out to the side in order to judge speed. It is also difficult to judge distances at night so be careful if you see stationary lights, as they may be nearer than they look. If in doubt about clearing an obstacle then always ask for assistance.

As part of your planning you will have checked the airfield charts and be aware of the available lighting at your airfield. *(See diagram page 289)*. Taxi lights may be available as blue edge lights or a green centre line. Carry out instrument checks during the taxy as for exercise 19.

Pre Take-Off Checks

At the holding point, ensure that your taxy light is not blinding the pilot on final approach. Use the navigation lights to check that the aircraft is not moving forward. This will be easier as there will be some reflection from the red and green lights to allow you to judge such movement. Carry out your power checks and pre-flight vital actions as normal using a dim setting for cabin light or your torch but ensuring that you protect your eyes from glare or too much white light. Once you have received clearance to line up on the runway, switch the landing light on and the strobes if fitted.

The Take-Off

Check the approach path carefully before entering the runway and then taxy on to the runway using all of its length. Ensure that the DI and compass are aligned and that all of the instrument indications are normal. In daylight you would normally pick a reference point ahead of you but this may be more difficult at night. Note the runway perspective, as it may look different in the dark. Carry out a visual take-off transferring your attention to the instruments immediately after you are airborne, since at this stage you will lose outside visual clues. Your climb out should be carried out solely by reference to instruments until at least 300 feet. Carry out the instrument scan for the climb. Do not try to turn until at a height of at least 500 feet a.g.l. Once established in the climb, switch off the landing light. Use a combination of visual flight to maintain your lookout and instrument flight to confirm attitude and heading until at a minimum safe altitude, for terrain clearance and to comply with Instrument Flight rules.

Night Orientation

Your instructor will initially guide you into the local area for "**night orientation**". You will note the aspect and perspective of the airfield as you leave the circuit. Note what the lights look like and look for any familiar landmarks which can be used for orientation. It may be difficult to see the features that you would normally expect during the day. As you depart the circuit you will notice the lights from roads and housing, but some of the terrain features may have disappeared from view. Water features may not be discernible if the night is not moonlit. Towns will appear to be nearer than they are but their shapes will stand out more clearly. High obstacles such as masts may be lit with red lights depending on their height.

You will find it easier to spot other aircraft as their navigation lights will show up and many aircraft use strobe lights. If you are near to controlled airspace it may be more difficult to work out which are commercial aircraft and which are light aircraft, but you will soon become accustomed to this. If there is a moon, then you may be able to pick out more features such as the outline of fields or hills. You will notice that there is little or no horizon although a coastline will be easily spotted if there is a built up area along it.

Return to the Airfield

When you initially return to the airfield, your instructor will give you a demonstration of the approach to the runway with a go around, in order to show the perspective and the use of the PAPIs or VASIs. As you join the circuit and fly downwind, it may be difficult to see the runway, since some runway lights are uni-directional and hard to pick out from the abeam position. You will note the airfield lights and it may be possible to see an aerodrome beacon flashing its two letter morse identification. *(Green for civilian and red for military).* Your instructor will fly the final approach to show you the use of the runway lights and approach lights to show you the correct, too high and too low approach picture. You will then go around initially on instruments to position downwind again *(see page 288)*.

On a normal circuit fly a combination of instrument and visual flying, remembering to maintain a good lookout at all times. Allow for drift downwind, being aware that at night there is the effect of diurnal variation so that the wind may be much stronger at altitude than it is on the ground and there could be a crosswind present that is not being forecast on the ground. Make the turn from downwind onto base leg in the normal position by reference to the runway lights and any approach lights available.

On final approach, using power to control your descent path and elevator to maintain the airspeed constant, use the PAPIs and any other runway lights to maintain a stable approach path. If there are no PAPIs fitted, then aim at a point approximately two to four runway lights in to the runway. Try not to get low on the approach at night, as you cannot be sure that you are clear of unlit obstacles in the approach path. Drift should be laid off as normal. Be prepared for windshear or changes of direction of the wind as you descend, as the wind is likely to back and decrease as you descend.

It is more difficult to judge the flare and roundout height at night. Use the runway lighting as a guide to the point to flare. As the ground appears to rise so that the lights are approaching your shoulder height then commence a gentle flare only slowly reducing the power. It is likely that your instructor will not let you use the landing light to start with. This is because it is very tempting to stare into the path of the landing light, which will not assist you in judging the flare. Try to look instead to the side of the nose, as this will assist you in judging your height. Gradually reduce the power in the flare and hold off so that the throttle is fully closed at touch down.

After landing keep straight and wait until the aircraft has slowed down before applying any brake. Use the runway lights to remain straight and taxi clear of the runway, stop and carry out your after landing checks as usual, using the torch and checklist if required.

Chapter 20 - Part 2

Night Navigation

20. **LESSON AIM**

      To navigate safely at night and to familiarise you with the limitations of visual features during the hours of darkness.

AIRMANSHIP

      Pre-flight etc. as before, Navigation: as day, but fewer features. Use towns, beacons, lighthouses, coastlines, moonlight. Position of North star, obstruction lights. IFR rules. Quadrantals, min alt for SVFR. MSA + 10nm. ATC flight plan on all longer night flights. Torch. Use thick/dark pen to write on log/map. Colours change with red light. Radio aids - check hours of operation. Check availability of alternates. More frequent radio calls. Recognition of weather deterioration. Emergencies.

Introduction

      The same principles apply as during the day, but there are a number of additional points to consider. It is difficult to estimate distances and difficult to see cloud before you are in it. At night the best ground features to use for navigation are towns and cities as they have distinctive patterns of lights. Large roads such as motorways are also useful, as are the aeronautical beacons at airfields. You should know your Morse code in order to use the latter meaningfully.

      If you plan to use radio navigation beacons, then ensure that you have checked the AIP for their operational hours. Remember the errors of NDBs -night effect, which is worst at dawn and dusk. Some radar services may not be available in the evening especially if based at a military airfield.

Planning

Make sure that you have checked the weather thoroughly for the route and the destination airfield. Be aware that if the temperature falls close to the dewpoint then the likelihood of mist and fog forming is greatly increased. Plan for a diversion airfield, remembering that many airfields will close at night. When selecting the route make sure that there are enough features to enable you to navigate effectively or that there are enough radio navigation aids to assist you. Make sure that the MSA for instrument flight rule compliance is available given the forecast weather. 1000 feet above the highest fixed obstacle within 5 nm of aircraft track is required.

Mark the flight log and the chart with a thick pen. Thin pencil writing is invisible in the dimmed light of the cockpit. Mark round the edges of towns and other features you are using for the navigation, as that will help the features stand out. Do not rely on any features which are marked in red on the chart. If necessary mark over them in black to make them stand out.

Calculate your fuel required and if weight is not a factor then take full tanks at night. Diversion airfields may be much further away than by day.

The Flight

Fly accurate headings. Bear in mind that distances are deceptive. Use the same techniques as during the day and keep an accurate log of ETA's and ATA's. Use the same techniques for establishing your position if lost. Use radio navigation aids to fix your position and if unable to fix it then call for assistance earlier rather than later. If the weather deteriorates forcing you to descend then divert or return to base without any hesitation. At night you are operating under IFR therefore you cannot safely descend and carry out a low level navigation exercise to return to the airfield. Ask for help from ATC. However, if you have planned correctly and taken note of the forecast weather then you should not end up in this situation.

Exercise 20 — Night Flying Emergencies

Night Flying Emergencies

LESSON AIM

To learn and practise Night Emergency Drills.

AIRMANSHIP

Lookout. Local Procedures. Alert ATC before practising any Emergency Drills.

AIR EXERCISE   *Emergencies that may occur.*

Minor Aircraft Emergencies

Failure of:
1) Navigation Light - Warn ATC.
2) Landing Light.
3) Anti-Collision Light.
4) Cockpit Lighting - Use a Torch.
5) Alternator - Load Shed.
6) Electrically Powered Flaps.
7) Gyro Suction - X Check Instruments.
8) Radio   1) Make Blind Transmissions.
          2) Squawk 7600
          3) Flash Landing Lights on Final

Action
1) If either Navigation Lights or Radio have failed fly a normal circuit remaining well clear of other aircraft.
2) Radio Failure, be prepared to go-around (at a safe height) while switching on/off landing light or navigation lights. If no red light is seen from the tower, or if the tower gives a green light, make a full stop landing. If no red light is seen, vacate the runway and taxi in.
3) Navigation lights and/or landing light failure - Make a full stop landing, vacate the runway and request assistance.

Major Aircraft Emergencies

1) **EFATO**
Not to be practised at night but during daytime, learn the safest areas to land in preparation for an EFATO.

Action
Should an EFATO or engine failure in the circuit occur at night, avoid illuminated areas and use the landing light to avoid obstructions.

2) **Total Electrical Failure**

Action
1) Keep well clear of other aircraft as they cannot see you.
2) Try recycling alternator field switch or circuit breaker.
3) Recycle Master Switch.
4) Fly over the tower at circuit height opening and closing the throttle.
5) If no red light from the tower or a green light is seen, fly a normal circuit and make a full stop landing. Pull clear of the runway shut down and wait for assistance.

3) **Engine Problem**
Rough running, high/low oil temperature, low oil pressure. Advise ATC.

Action
Fly a circuit within gliding distance of the runway, land and taxi in.

Continued Overleaf ...

LESSON AIM

To learn and practise Night Emergency Drills.

AIRMANSHIP

Lookout. Local Procedures. Alert ATC before practising any Emergency Drills.

AIR EXERCISE   *Emergencies that may occur.*

Surface Emergencies

1) Total Power Failure on the Aerodrome

May be over a wide area.

Action

1) Follow local orders. If possible - orbit present position and wait for the standby radio. Check fuel state.
2) If lights are out for a protracted period-divert.

2) Approach Path Indicator Failure

Action

1) Inform ATC.
2) If Solo - Make a full stop landing.
3) If Dual - Instructor's decision whether to land or continue with the detail.

3) ATC Radio Failure

Action

1) Fly normal circuits at circuit height making position calls downwind and final approach.
2) Wait for standby radio to come on line.

4) Flarepath Failure

Action

1) Fly normal circuits at normal circuit height and await ATC instructions.
2) Be prepared to divert as directed by ATC.

Quiz No. 20

1. Extra equipment is required for flying at night eg. ......

2. A good precaution to adopt before starting the engine is to ......

3. At the holding point it is good airmanship to ...... the landing light to ...... pilots.

4. The Climb Out at night to at least 300 feet should be effected by ......

5. Before Night Navigation, you should prepare your chart more carefully because colours such as ...... and ...... will not show up.

6. Emergencies at night will be practised, including failures of ......, ..., ... total .... and emergencies on the airfield.

Answers

No. 20

1. A Torch and Spare Batteries.
2. Switch the Landing Light On and Off several times.
3. Switch Off, Avoid Dazzling other.
4. Sole Reference to Instruments.
5. Red, Yellow.
6. Navigation Lights, Landing Lights, Radio, Electrical Failure.

Index

T